For
Ally
Enjoy these
Enjoy stories from
Miracle stories from
the UGA VTH!

Ron Henson

To all the pets we've loved before, we love now and will love in the future.

Text copyright © 2017 by Rachel Rowena Henson

First U.S. edition 2017

ISBN 978-0-9896224-1-7

Library of Congress Control Number: 2017907151

Printed and bound in Malaysia for Tryptic

Designed by SUSAK PRESS
www.susakpress.org

Edited by Alison Tinsley

Copy edited by Elizabeth Wright for Tryptic

While meeting with many of these special miracle story
animals and owners, I was able to take the majority of
pictures in the book myself.

For the animals no longer with us and with those
that I wasn't able to meet personally, the animal
owners graciously shared their favorite photos with me.
You know who you are and I thank you for your
contribution. Some of the amazing photographs were
taken by professional photographers. In particular,
I'd like to recognize the following:

Squishy - Kym Chamber Photography
Justin - Aly Rattazzi/Rather Be Riding Photography
Alder - Christina Power Photography
Asa - Alecia Lauren Photography
Cherokee - Jennifer Lindell and Chris Herron
Mackenzie - David Richards and Harvin Alert
Anya - Kristina Pearson from the Racine Zoo

Special thanks to the photographers at the UGA VTH
for Norman & Vera photo and building photographs:
Whitney Mathisen, Jaime Curtis and Sue Myers Smith.

© 2015 University of Georgia Photographer: Peter Frey
for new Veterinary School surgery picture

If I've omitted credit to other professionals whose photos
were included, it was in no way intentional.

Miracles on College Station Road

Survival Stories from the University of Georgia Veterinary Teaching Hospital

By Row Henson

CONTENTS

In Memory of
Mackenzie (Mac) Henson

Mac came into my life when she was two years old. She belonged to a friend of mine, who traveled often. Mac spent much of her early years either at a kennel being trained to hunt ducks or in the back of her owner's truck. Before she met me, she had never been inside a house.

I grew up with dogs and had a number of them over my lifetime but I had a job that required much travel so a dog had been out of the question for me for a number of years. In 2001, I was diagnosed with cancer. As anyone who has gone through a serious health issue knows, this diagnosis changes your life. I decided that my health needed to take priority over work and my employer graciously allowed me to work part time so I might try to better balance my life. Since I was not traveling as much, I suggested to my friend that I might help him out by keeping Mac when he needed to travel. The rest is – as they say – history.

When Mac's owner came to pick her up between his travels, she sat by me and looked up with a "do I really have to go" look. Being the well-trained dog that she was, she went – but I knew each time her heart stayed with me.

A few days after the last time Mac's owner picked her up, I received a call from him. Mac had stopped eating and he told me he'd realized she was no longer his dog. So he brought her back to me and the home she loved. That was twelve years ago. I like to say that Mac was a rescue dog, rescued from a life in the back of a truck. But the real truth is that Mac rescued me. Our lives were far better together than they had been before we met.

Mac was a black American Labrador Retriever and, like most retrievers, she loved to retrieve. Anything! Her early training had taught her how to retrieve ducks, but she quickly adapted to frisbees, balls, bumpers, sticks, or pretty much anything that could be thrown, picked up and, most importantly, returned so that she could go through the process over (and over and over) again. My arm tired long before Mac ever said stop.

Ten years ago, I fulfilled a lifelong dream of buying a property in the South of France and Mac and I began spending six months a year there. The second year we were there, while retrieving a frisbee, Mac tore her CCL (Cranial Cruciate Ligament) and we returned to the United States where Mac was treated by Dr. Ken Greenwood, her local Orthopedic Veterinary Surgeon, with TPLO (Tibial Plateau Leveling Osteotomy) surgery. She did very well until a couple of years later when she began to show lameness in the other rear leg. Thinking that she had torn the other CCL, we returned to the Orthopedic Veterinarian only to find out that, instead of another ligament tear, she most likely had lumbosacral disease. This is when we were referred to the UGA VTH. We didn't know it then, but that introduction would change our lives forever.

We first came to the school in February 2011 and saw Dr. Marc Kent who confirmed Mac's diagnosis. Like many athletes, the years of physical activity had taken a toll on Mac's body. I have said to myself often that if I knew then what I know now I would have limited her activity, but I know that Mac would not have wanted it any different – even though she paid a price for her fun in her later years.

Dr. Kent recommended a regimen of medication to help relieve Mac's pain and reduce the inflammation brought on from  her lumbosacral disease, arthritis, and degenerating discs. For several years, this gave Mac a relatively normal life and we continued traveling to our home in France. In the summer of 2013, Mac again began to show signs of lameness and, after receiving a diagnosis of a herniated disc from the Toulouse Veterinary School, we returned to the UGA VTH. Under the care of our now friend, Dr. Kent, Mac had surgery to relieve the disc (L7-S1) herniation. The ever resilient Mac, once again, began to live a relatively normal life for an aging Labrador.

Mac had many issues over her long life, multiple soft tissue sarcomas removed from her rear legs, multiple diaspores (wild grass seeds) removed from her lungs (a common occurrence in the country side of France) and, finally, a diagnosis of laryngeal paralysis in the fall of 2014. After that diagnosis we again returned to the amazing staff at the UGA VTH when the laryngeal paralysis began to severely affect Mac's ability to breathe. In the spring of 2015, tracheostomy surgery was performed on Mac by Dr. Karen Cornell. This gave Mac immediate relief and she lived another year thanks to the amazing staff at the UGA VTH.

Earlier this year, at the age of fifteen, Mac let me know it was her time to go. She looked directly at me with an "I've done everything you've ever asked of me – but now I'm asking you to let me go" look. And then she looked away and died in the arms of six members of the UGA VTH – people who had loved and cared for her over the many years of additional life she had been given, thanks to their amazing talent and dedication.

I donated Mac's body to the school and her bones were reconstructed to help students see firsthand the effects of arthritis and disc disease on animals. Mac now remains a permanent fixture in the place that helped give her such a long and full life.

Mac's story and the others you will read about in these pages were my inspiration for creating this book. So many of our beloved pets have been given second chances thanks to the knowledge and dedication of the staff at the University of Georgia Veterinary Teaching Hospital. It is my privilege to help tell them to you.

Introduction to the University of Georgia Veterinary Teaching Hospital

The experience of bringing an animal to the Veterinary Teaching Hospital (VTH) begins much like an appointment at any veterinary hospital. What is most unusual is the sheer size of the VTH. While the size of the VTH can be intimidating, the hospital functions much like any veterinary hospital with some very notable exceptions. Here is a little guide to help navigate the VTH.

One of the most common questions people have is, why would you go to the University of Georgia (UGA), College of Veterinary Medicine, Veterinary Teaching Hospital? To start, it is helpful to understand what the VTH is. The University is divided into many Colleges, one of which is the College of Veterinary Medicine. The College has many missions, including research and investigation into animal disorders, education of the next generation of veterinarians, and public service. The Veterinary Teaching Hospital is involved in all three of these missions. In the process of providing veterinary care to animals brought to the VTH, students are taught and valuable information is gained that contributes to future clinical investigations.

So, why would someone bring an animal to the VTH? And how does someone make an appointment? While there are many veterinary practices, there are only a few that provide specialized care for animals. The VTH is staffed by veterinarians who are the experts in numerous fields. Many are at the cutting edge of what veterinary medicine and surgery can offer and many others are actively searching for newer and better ways of diagnosing and treating patients. In addition, the VTH has the most modern and state of the art equipment in the country, even rivaling many of the modern hospitals for people! Your veterinarian can call and arrange for you to get an appointment. In an emergency, the VTH has an entire staff dedicated to providing 24 hour care, seven days a week, year round.

To understand how this all works, it is helpful to understand the logistics of the hospital and to learn about the people (students, veterinarians, and veterinary nurses) who provide care for patients.

The VTH is divided into two parts: one side is for small animals (dogs, cats, all kinds of birds, reptiles, ferrets, rabbits and other small pets) and the other side is for large animals (horses, cows, llamas, alpacas, and other farm animals). Upon arrival to the Small Animal Teaching Hospital, you and your pet are greeted by the front desk staff and offered seating in the main lobby or in an alcove along a long hallway outside of examination rooms. The large animal hospital has its own waiting room for check-in. Once checked in, the "service" (medical team) that you have scheduled an appointment with will be notified of your arrival.

Navigating the Veterinary Teaching Hospital is a little like "What's behind door #2?" Most often, the first person you meet for your appointment is a veterinary doctoral student (enrolled in the Doctorate of Veterinary Medicine [DVM] curriculum). Although still a student, he or she is one year or less away from being a veterinarian. To reach the point of meeting you, the student will have completed a four-year undergraduate degree, often a Bachelors of Science or Bachelors of Arts degree, and have advanced through three years of his or her DVM degree at UGA. Now in the final part of training, he or she will play an integral role in your experience. In large part, the fourth year student you work with is the most important part of your experience as he or she provides an essential link in communication between the doctors and you.

Having met your student, you enter an exam room through Door #1. Much like your regular veterinarian or your own physician, your student will discuss your pet's medical history and ask you questions to help clarify your pet's condition. Following this discussion, the veterinary student and your pet will leave through Door #2 on the other side of the room. Before explaining what happens behind Door #2, it is helpful to understand who the people providing care for your pet are.

Both the large and small animal sections are divided into numerous specialized services focused in particular areas of medicine and surgery. For most people, their regular (primary) veterinarian is a general practitioner who has a wide breadth of knowledge and experience and provides outstanding care. In some complex cases, a greater level of expertise or specialized equipment may be necessary for optimal therapy. In these cases, your regular veterinarian will refer you to the VTH to seek out a veterinarian specialized in your pet's particular condition. In the small animal hospital, specializations include services providing care in internal medicine, orthopedic surgery, general surgery, neurology and neurosurgery, cardiology, oncology (medical and radiation oncology), dermatology, ophthalmology, zoological medicine, behavior, and emergency and critical care medicine. In the large animal hospital, specializations include services providing care in internal medicine, surgery, farm practice (a service that makes farm calls), theriogenology/ reproductive medicine, and emergency and critical care medicine.

In addition, there are numerous veterinarians who provide specialized services like diagnostic imaging (studies like X rays, ultrasonography, computer tomography [CT] scans, and magnetic resonance imaging [MRI]), anesthesia, clinical pathology (veterinarians specializing in the interpretation of diagnostic tests often involving microscopic evaluation of specimens) and anatomic pathology (veterinarians involved in the interpretation of biopsy specimens). Most of these vets work behind the scenes and, while you are unlikely to meet them, they are essential in providing the best care for the patients at the VTH.

Who are the personnel on a service? The team is led by a College faculty member who is a board certified veterinarian in a specific area of medicine or surgery. Board certification is a postgraduate, 3-year advanced degree program that a veterinarian can pursue. In hospitals for people, such individuals may be considered the "attending" doctors. Other veterinarians on the service may include an intern or resident. Interns are veterinarians who, following graduation from a DVM program, enter a one year intensive clinical training program focused on small- or large-animal medicine and surgery. Often, an internship is the stepping-stone toward more focused specialization gained through a residency program. Residency programs are usually 3 years long and provide the training to become board certified. At UGA, residencies are highly competitive and typically one individual a year, out of a pool of hundreds, is accepted. Finally, each service, as well as the Hospital wards (where hospitalized patients stay), have certified veterinary nurses who provide the lion's share of the care of patients. The nursing staff of the VTH are among the most compassionate and dedicated people you can imagine. They all go the extra mile to care for the animals.

As an animal leaves through Door #2, it is brought to the specific service's examination area. There, your pet's medical team is assembled to perform an exam. The examination is done under the guidance of the faculty member.

After a thorough examination, the student, intern or resident, and faculty member engage in intensive discussion about your pet's medical history, your pet's physical examination, and the diagnostic tests run by your veterinarian. In large part, these intensive discussions are how clinical veterinary medical education is provided to students but, most important, your pet gets the benefit of having multiple people all working to determine which potential diseases or disorders may be affecting your pet, how best to diagnose the problem, what treatments should be considered, and ultimately the prognosis.

As you can imagine, these kind of in-depth discussions take time. From your perspective, it often seems like an eternity but, following a comprehensive exam and discussion about how best to provide your pet's care, a few members of the service will return and discuss exam findings and options for further tests or therapies to treat your pet. Often, your pet will be admitted to the hospital. During its hospitalization, you will be updated about your pet's condition by the doctors of the service but much of the communications will run through your student who will provide daily updates, inform you about test results, and provide logistical aspects such as when visiting hours are and when you can come to pick up your pet.

In the end, the benefit of coming to the VTH is that an entire team of doctors are focused on your pet. You will receive individualized attention working through a student to ensure that you know your pet's condition. All the doctors, from the faculty leading the service to the interns, residents, and students, are dedicated to providing compassionate care and state-of-the-art expert medical care. The stories told in the pages that follow are but a few of the many miracles that happen at the VTH. They are a testament to all the passionate individuals working every day to help animals.

Name:

Cody

Owners:

Kathy Watts
Danny Watts

SHETLAND SHEEPDOG
Age: 15
Address: NICHOLSON, GA

Condition:

Nose Cancer

Cody
Beauty is Only Skin Deep

Cody has a special place in my heart. He gave me the original idea for this book. When I was at the UGA VTH when my dog was scheduled for surgery, Cody was also there having surgery and we were assigned the same student, Will Basinger. Will explained to me that they were running behind because they were involved in a very long and complicated surgery for a dog that had part of his nose and face removed followed by a kind of plastic surgery to have what remained become his "new" nose. That dog was Cody. As a standard follow up to surgery (just like with people), the surgeon likes to do an appointment two weeks following the animal's release. I returned with my dog and, just as we were getting out of the car, another car pulled into the parking lot. A dog jumped out and came over to me wagging his tail. I knew that this was the dog with part of his face missing. I said to his owner, "You don't know me, but I know your dog. He was having surgery while my dog was here." The owner answered, "It's a miracle. He is the happiest dog in the world. He has no idea he is missing part of his face." I responded, "Can't we all learn valuable lessons from our pets." I came home and kept thinking that Cody's story, along with so many other miracles performed by the UGA VTH, needed to be told. Thank you, Cody, for your inspiration.

As the book idea took formation and I started contacting the "miracle stories", Cody's was at the top of my list. Cody's surgery took over seven hours and required the removal of most of the upper portion of his nose and mouth. He had to have teeth removed and learn how to eat from the back instead of the front of his mouth. Kathy started him off with soft food but, being ever-resilient, he quickly adapted to eating his normal diet from the very back of his mouth.

I was able to have a long visit with his owners, Kathy and Danny Watts, as well as Cody and his younger companions, Jake and Sadie, also Shelties. At the end of our visit, we went outside where Cody showed me that at 15 years of age, he could still run and fetch his ball. It was truly amazing to see how he had not only relearned how to eat, but also how to pick up the ball from the very back of his "half a face." His two-year old companions had a hard time keeping up with him and one thing was for sure – he was the head dog in the Watts house: both smart and still beautiful.

Name:
Amber

Owners:
Joyce Davis Cunningham
Joe Cunningham

MIXED BREED GOAT
Age: 9
Address: LANDRUM, SC

Condition:
Abscess and infection behind
right eye, pituitary tumor,
other misc. issues

Amber
Surrounded by Guardian Angels

Amber was about six months old when she arrived at Joyce and Joe's farm. Little did they know then, but they had taken in an animal that would need multiple surgeries over the next few years. One week after her arrival, Amber had an accident that ripped her right horn off leaving a gaping hole in its place. She also tore off a large part of her right nostril and about half of each ear. The healing process for all Amber's injuries took weeks but, six months after the accident, an abscess developed behind her right eye. Amber's regular veterinarian had been in contact with the staff at UGA VTH and they agreed to examine Amber. In early January 2012, Amber was welcomed by the staff of the Large Animal Hospital at the University of Georgia. She was treated like a high profile goat, not the mixed breed, one-horned, half-eared, swollen-eyed, pathetic creature she appeared to be. The decision was made to operate on the eye but, in order to remove the abscess, the eye also had to be removed. After a few days, Amber came home and adapted very quickly to life with one eye.

Amber was faced with another problem while recovering. Her udder was growing larger and it was obvious that she was producing milk. Amber's local veterinarian worked for a couple of weeks trying to get her condition under control. Finally, the veterinarian suggested Amber be taken back the UGA VTH. She was welcomed at the hospital and made to feel at home in the same stall she had occupied earlier.

Tests showed she had cystic follicles on her ovaries. Amber underwent a laparoscopic ovariectomy and both ovaries were removed. She was released and came home with a strict diet (no more collards and cornbread), limited activities, and instructions to measure and record the size of her udder. After a short period of time, it became obvious that the milk production had not stopped. The doctors became suspicious that a pituitary tumor was causing the combination of neurologic signs as she was acting mentally abnormal as well as displaying inappropriate lactation and mammary enlargement. The pituitary gland is a gland at the base of the brain that produces various hormones, including those involving lactation. Amber had an MRI performed which also showed that there was still infection in her eye socket. On Amber's arrival back at the Large Animal Hospital, she got out of the trailer and once again led the way to the stall that had become her home-away-from-home. Amber was welcomed and settled in for her stay. Her doctors located and removed Amber's enlarged mammary tissue and an abscess deep behind her eye socket.

Amber's mom, Joyce, believes that our animals have guardian angels watching over them, some of whom are the staff "angels" at the VTH. Joyce and Joe took Amber home several days later and, this time, she quickly recovered. Today, thanks to the devoted, hard-working, professional veterinarians and staff at the UGA VTH, Amber is once again enjoying a wonderful life on Mountainview Berry Farm.

Name:
Thor

Owners:
Angela Fusaro
Jeff Eliason

GOLDEN RETRIEVER MIX
Age: 3
Address: ATLANTA, GA

Condition:
Dysfunctional Bladder
Sphincter

Thor One Lucky Rescue

Angela and Jeff adopted Thor from Golden Retriever Rescue of Atlanta. They saw the litter of eight online and, as a surprise for Angela, Jeff called to see if he might visit and look at them. "Fred" was the runt of the litter and the last of the eight to be adopted. They brought him home and renamed him Thor Muggin Fusiason. He was a lover from the beginning and fit right in; however, they soon noticed that Thor was leaking urine. Angela and Jeff, both physicians, knew the problem was more than just a house-breaking issue. Their local veterinarian started Thor on antibiotics and a special diet for possible urethral stones but it didn't help. Their veterinarian then recommended they meet with the specialists at the UGA Veterinary Teaching Hospital.

Angela and Jeff took Thor to the Hospital and met with Dr. Chad Schmiedt, faculty on the General surgery service. Dr. Schmiedt recommended a computer tomography (CT scan) as he suspected that Thor was born with ectopic ureters. The ureters are small tubes that connect the kidneys to the bladder. In some dogs, instead of emptying into the bladder, the tubes empty into the urethra bypassing the urethral sphincter. The CT scan enabled Dr. Schmiedt to make a more definitive diagnosis of a dysfunctional urethral sphincter, a congenital condition seen most often in female dogs. Baby Thor, born in July, rescued in September, was getting ready for surgery in November. At surgery, Dr. Schmiedt could see that the sphincter muscle hadn't developed properly and the surgical treatment involved reinforcing the sphincter muscle with a device that mimics the muscle. Angela waited at the hospital for Thor to get out of surgery but Jeff had to work late. He so wanted to check on his boy that the surgery resident working with Dr. Schmiedt kindly met him after hours. Angela and Jeff were able to take Thor home the next day. Dr. Schmiedt indicated that there was a chance that the surgery might not be effective or could take a few days to start working. Thor was a champ and recovered fully: no more leaking. Great news for both Thor and his parents!

A year later, Angela and Jeff noticed that Thor was now having the opposite problem. He was straining to try and urinate with no results. They returned to their local veterinarian who passed a urethral catheter to empty Thor's bladder of urine and kept it in Thor as they returned to the UGA VTH. They returned to Dr. Schmiedt who performed surgery the same day. He found a blockage in the urinary tract from a blood clot. The blood clot was removed along with the device that had been reinforcing the sphincter muscle. It seems that the device was doing too good a job, so it was decided that they would see if the muscle would now function without reinforcement. Success! That was over six months ago and Thor is doing great. When I met him, it was clear to me that Thor is a well adjusted, happy and affectionate young dog with a great life ahead of him, thanks to loving parents and the wonderful staff and faculty at the UGA VTH.

Name:
Bugsy

Owners:
Bill Kress
Melanie Kress

MOLUCCAN COCKATOO
Age: 25
Address: COMMERCE, GA

Condition:
Broken wing
Blood transfusion from
blood loss during surgery

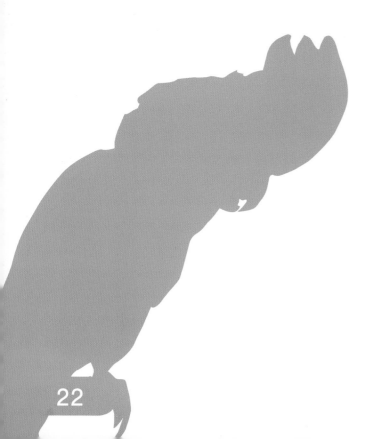

Bugsy
A Cockatoo
That Gives a Hoot

After visiting the famous Bugsy, I knew immediately that if I ever come back as a bird I want to live with Melanie and Bill Kress. What impressed me even more than their lovely home though, was the aviary they built for the many birds they have rescued over the years. The aviary is a free-standing building with its own heating and air conditioning so the birds stay comfortable year round! Every morning, they are treated to special foods including macadamia nuts. They sing and chat constantly, and why shouldn't they? Melanie and Bill are avid lovers of all animals, especially those in need of a home. All the birds, as well as a number of cats, have found refuge in this amazing spot.

Bill Kress has a special fondness for birds because of his lifelong career as a magician. He often worked his magic by pulling doves from his hat so, as you might guess, he has many doves in his aviary as well as other exotic varieties. He and Melanie rescued Bugsy, a Moluccan Cockatoo, when she was five years old.

In 2011, Bugsy had an accident and broke her wing. Their family veterinarian took one look and said, "You need an expert and the best around is at UGA." So Bill and Bugsy headed to Athens. During the surgery, Bugsy lost so much blood that the surgeon, Dr. Mayer, told Bill an immediate transfusion was needed in order to keep Bugsy alive. But where would one find a Moluccan Cockatoo on such short notice? Amazingly, a few days earlier, someone had found an injured owl and taken it to the UGA VTH. Dr. Mayer suggested that they check to see if a transfusion from the owl might work and, incredibly, it did. Bugsy perked up immediately. The owl transfusion bought her enough time to find an exact donor. Bugsy is not only singing for her breakfast now, but she gives a good hoot on an occasional dark night.

Bill and Melanie were so thankful to the staff at the UGAVTH that they created the Bill and Melanie Kress Fund for Wildlife and Zoological Medicine to help inspire students to learn more in the area of avian medicine. Thanks to their contribution, an avian ward has been built. It is affectionately referred to as the Bugsy Wing.

Amazing gift from amazing people, but then birds of a feather do flock together.

Name:
Harley

Owners:
**Kris Wiggins
Thor Wiggins**

GOLDEN RETRIEVER MIX
Age: 12
Address: MCDONOUGH, GA

Condition:
Multilobular bone cancer,
radiation.
Severe ear infection

Harley *Flea Market Bargain, Lottery Jackpot*

Kris and Thor found Harley while visiting a local Flea Market. He was with a litter of 12-week old Golden Retriever mix puppies and he weighed a whopping 3 ½ pounds. The $20 they paid for Harley was the best investment they made that day.

At the time, Thor was living in McDonough and Kris lived in North Carolina. In 2012, Kris and Thor had already planned their wedding and honeymoon when one of their friends, while petting Harley, said, "What is this lump on Harley's head?" Harley was a long-haired blond, so it hadn't been noticeable. When their local veterinarian couldn't aspirate the lump, they took an x-ray and referred Harley to the Oncology Department at the UGA VTH. After additional tests were taken, Harley was diagnosed with a very rare bone cancer – multilobular tumor of the bone, which typically grows on flat bones such as those of the skull. The Oncologists recommended surgery, followed by radiation therapy. All of this took place just weeks before Kris and Thor's wedding. We all know that weddings and surgeries are both expensive propositions, so the couple decided to cancel their honeymoon to stay home and help Harley during his recovery. They weren't sure where the money would come from for the surgery and radiation, but they knew they had to do everything possible to save Harley. Their prayers were answered when Thor called Kris to tell her he had hit the lottery – literally! The payout was almost the exact amount for the surgery and radiation on Harley.

Dr. Kent performed the craniectomy surgery and the majority of the tumor was successfully removed. The small amount that remained was treated with four weeks of radiation therapy. Every Monday, they would take Harley for his weekly trip to Athens. He did well for the first three weeks, but had difficulty with the last week so Thor took the last week off work to stay home with Harley and make sure he was as comfortable as possible. For the next 2 ½ years, they returned to the UGA VTH initially every 3 months, then every 6 months. They finally graduated to annual checkups.

In May of 2016, Harley's check up was clear, but when they returned in November of 2016 the CT scan showed re-growth in the bone cancer. They were given options: 1) another surgery 2) radiation or 3) do nothing. They did not want to put Harley through another surgery, so they opted for the less invasive radiation therapy. Once again, the Monday after Thanksgiving, Harley started back on five days a week of radiation for four weeks. A few weeks after finishing radiation therapy, Harley developed a severe ear infection and TECA (Total Ear Canal Ablation) surgery was performed to remove the vertical and horizontal ear canals down to the middle ear and the middle ear was cleaned with lateral bulla osteotomy.

Harley is home once again with a clean bill of health and happy parents who so love their flea market bargain and who are deeply grateful to their team at the UGA VTH (and the lottery!)

Name:
Ferdnan

Owner:
Henry Morris

ANGUS BULL
Age: 25
Address: BAXLEY, GA

Condition:
Broken leg

Fertile Ferdnan the Bull

Henry's family has been in the cattle business for several generations. When Henry went online to check out some young Angus calves that were getting ready to be sold, he was taken by one particular yearling and decided to visit him in person. He rubbed the young bull's head and said, "If you don't cost too much, I'm going to take you home with me." $6,150 later, the two headed back to Henry's farm. Bull #25 fit right in with the other cattle, in excess of 300 head including eight bulls.

Bull #25 went on to become one of Henry's finest purchases and is the father to many offspring. Henry says that during breeding season the bulls can become very aggressive as they try to eliminate their competition. In many cases, a bull is most vulnerable when he is mounting a cow. Henry suspects that this was the case with Bull #25 when he found him lying down with a broken tibia (shin bone).

Henry thought he would have to shoot the bull as that is a common occurrence with a large herd, but he just couldn't go there with the best bull he ever owned so he called his county agent who directed Henry to the UGA VTH. He drove Bull #25 there that night and was met by Dr. Eggleston and his team who took the bull in for evaluation. Radiographs revealed a severely comminuted fracture (bone broken into multiple pieces) of the tibia. Based on his size, surgical repair of the severely broken bone was not an option. Fortunately, there is a technique that can be used to partially stabilize a limb in hopes of healing the fracture. Bull #25 was placed under general anesthesia and a full-limb cast was placed on the limb in combination with a Thomas-Shroeder splint. This allows a bull to walk without bearing full weight on the fractured limb. During the three months that Bull #25 was at the hospital, he became a favorite of the staff and students and they nicknamed him Ferdnan. Unfortunately for Ferdnan, when the cast was finally removed, there was a draining abscess overlying where the bone was broken. This was worrisome as an infection could inhibit the fracture from healing which would be life threatening. Henry wasn't about to give up now! Ferdnan was put under anesthesia, the abscess was drained and a small piece of dead bone was removed. A second cast was placed and the splint re-applied. Fortunately, there were no complications. Ten days later, Ferdnan went home. During hospitalization, Henry says he visited Ferdnan as often as possible but, at the time, Henry also had a broken leg. Just wish I had gotten a picture of the two of them together with their casts on!

Henry says the staff was amazing and called every day over the three months Ferdnan was in the hospital to keep him updated on Ferdnan's progress. He also says that Ferdnan did not make it the full year away from "the ladies" as the vet school had recommended, but his leg is holding up just fine. Fertile Ferdnan has many offspring that have more than paid for both his purchase fee and his veterinary bills!

Name:
Squishy

Owner:
Renay Gregoire

AMERICAN BULLDOG, BORDER COLLIE, BOSTON TERRIER, STAFFORDSHIRE TERRIER MIX
Age: 2
Address: ATHENS, GA

Condition:
Injury from being tied up and other complications, paw amputation

My Squishy

Renay works at the Athens Area Humane Society and was on a rescue mission to pick up some puppies from the Toccoa-Stephens County Humane Shelter. Squishy was not even on the radar, but she had been rescued by Toccoa-Stephens County Humane Shelter from an abandoned property earlier that day with her mother and eight other surviving siblings. Squishy's mother and most of her siblings were unharmed, but Squishy and another sibling were wrapped in twine and, although the other sibling died, Squishy held on. The animal control officer came out to tell Renay that it was a sad day because it looked like they would have to euthanize the injured runt of the litter. He came out of the office toting a kitty litter pan with a badly injured pup inside wrapped in a blanket. The rest of the story is how a terribly injured puppy became Renay's Squishy.

On the way home from the rescue mission, Renay and Jed Kaylor, the Athens Area Humane Society shelter manager, discussed the badly injured puppy's paw. Renay said, "Ewww – her paw is so squishy. The two immediately recalled a quote from Dory in *Finding Nemo*, "I will call him Squishy and he will be my Squishy." Thus Squishy became her name and her mother and litter mates were also named after characters in *Finding Nemo*.

Renay and Jed took Squishy to the South Athens Animal Clinic where she was initially treated and Renay began the long journey of nursing Squishy back to health. When Renay realized that her paw was not going to heal and was literally "loose" with skin coming off and exposing bone, she rushed Squishy to the UGA VTH Emergency Clinic. The emergency staff and veterinarians/residents almost certainly saved Squishy's life by providing trauma care including IVs, pain medication and proper sterile bandaging. The paw was so damaged that it eventually fell off.

Squishy still had an uphill battle with three additional surgeries performed by the Humane Society's veterinarian and countless hours of special care. Renay was Squishy's primary caregiver. She went to work with Renay every day and everyone that came into contact with Squishy fell in love with her. Today, she is the mascot of the Athens Area Humane Society. Even though literally thousands of people hearing Squishy's story wanted to adopt her, she is "officially" Renay's dog. She is alive because of Renay's diligent efforts to save a 2 ½ pound dog that was minutes away from euthanization. She is now two years old weighing in at fifty pounds and loves everyone she meets and, oh my, does everyone love her. Renay says that Squishy is the most endearing and resilient animal she has ever met. I would say that these two are incredibly lucky to have found each other.

Follow Squishy on Instagram @call.me.squishy.

Name:
Justin

Owner:
India Wilkinson

QUARTER HORSE GELDING
Age: 18
Address: ALPHARETTA, GA

Condition:
Right Hock injury severing lower hock joints, extensor tendons and bone damage

Justin *India's Heart*

India is an avid equestrian who had saved for years for her dream horse. That horse was Justin. She knew immediately that he had all the attributes she was looking for: kind eyes, a stunning black coat and amazing athleticism. She bought him in January, 2004, when he was six years old. Six months later, all was going perfectly in his lessons and in the show ring. He even welcomed India's three year old daughter for rides. Everything came to a screeching halt on July 4th when the call that every horse owner dreads came. "There's been an accident." Justin had been spooked by fireworks and had jumped an electric fence catching and cutting through tissue, muscle, tendons and into the bone. By the time India could get to Justin, he was lying on his side with his leg the size of a tree trunk. After consulting her local veterinarian, India made the decision to rush Justin to the UGA VTH. An emergency ambulance service was arranged to help Justin travel more comfortably and to avoid further injury.

Justin and India were met by members of the staff, including Dr. John Peroni, at the Large Animal Hospital. After the massive wounds had been cleaned, India was told that, if there was any hope of saving Justin, immediate surgery would have to be performed. Even then the odds were not in his favor. The doctors were concerned that infection had already entered the bone of his hock (ankle). India, still in shock, says she remembers only saying, "Do whatever you need to do to save him." Dr. Peroni performed the surgery that saved Justin's life and the horse began a long recovery process which included a combined total of 32 weeks in the hospital and rehabilitation farm. He underwent two major surgeries, countless standing procedures, and skin grafting. Justin fought off bone infection, colic, laminitis (founder), kidney failure, muscle atrophy, stomach ulcers and depression.

He was given a prognosis of a 5% chance to live but, even if he did survive, there was also a chance that he might never have a full life. Justin defied the odds with the incredible care of the UGA VTH team. Justin's sweet personality and his resilience is inspiring and has made him a favorite at the hospital even to this day. Justin is now 18 years old and is enjoying life in the country on a 100 acre farm with his buddies. He comes running whenever he sees India driving into the farm. India says that animals are sent to us to teach us life lessons and Justin's lesson was that survival is always possible. India and Justin's story certainly illustrates this. I had the pleasure of meeting Justin and, after feeding him carrots and apples, I can see why he is India's heart as I also left a part of mine there with him.

Name:
Alder Agnew

Owners:
Christina Agnew
Todd Agnew

SPRINGER SPANIEL
Age: 5
Address: MITCHELL, GA

Condition:
Pyothorax

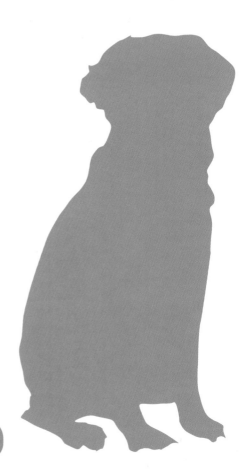

Alder Agnew
the Blue Ribbon Dog

Alder is a blue ribbon winning dog in many ways. At the age of three, he had already won a number of field trials and was considered one of the top 15 field trial dogs in the country. While returning home from a competition in New York, Alder began to show signs of distress and Christina and Todd Agnew were so concerned that they drove Alder to the closest emergency clinic. The emergency clinic lacked ultrasound capabilities and were unable to determine the exact cause of the distress so they recommended that Alder be taken immediately to the emergency care unit at the University of Georgia VTH. The Agnews turned around and drove several more hours to the VTH where they were greeted by the students and doctors prepared to take Alder in for evaluation.

Alder was diagnosed with pyothorax – a serious infection in his chest cavity. The lung is the organ that enables the exchange of gases between the blood stream and the air that we breathe. The lung is divided into a right and left lung each of which is further divided into lobes. To keep the lungs inflated with air, there is negative pressure within the chest cavity but outside of the lungs. This negative pressure is within the pleural cavity that exists between the chest wall and the outside of the lungs themselves. Pyothorax is an infection that develops in the pleural cavity and results in pus that builds up around the lung. The negative pressure is released and the lungs may collapse making breathing difficult. The infection typically, but not always, is caused by a foreign body such as a stick, seed pod, that punctures into the pleural cavity and brings with it bacteria that sets up an infection. For Alder, pyothorax was impacting his ability to breathe. The doctors explained various options, including a minimally invasive and less expensive procedure of trying to drain the infection and a more extensive surgery to look for the cause of the bacterial infection, lavage the infection within the pleural cavity, and then treat the infection with antibiotics. Christina and Todd initially decided on the less invasive option. When that did not prove successful, the Alders were faced with a decision. Alder is a working dog raised and trained by his owner who is also the owner of Craney Hill Kennel. Todd has a number of dogs and lots of expenses. Cost of surgery is always a concern. Alder was young and otherwise in good health, but the survival rate for this surgery is statistically low. His owners made the decision to progress with the surgery. "Yes" for the surgery from his Mom and "no" from his Dad. We all know how that decision ended!

The recovery for this surgery is typically from five to seven days, but Alder, being the blue ribbon dog that he is, was up and ready to go home in only two days. Thanks to the excellent care and quick action of both Alder's owners and the UGA VTH staff, Alder is now back in action, and preparing to compete for the National Championship!

Name:
Dolly

Owner:
Danette Kennedy

DOMESTIC CAT
Age: 4
Address: ALPHARETTA, GA

Condition:
Arousal Based Aggression

Dolly
Sometime Doll,
Sometime Stalker

After Danette's cat and dog both died within a two month period she decided to go to Forsyth Animal Control to rescue a cat. There were so many cats to pick from that Danette visited three days in a row to decide which one would be right for her. Dolly was eight months old and Danette knew she was the one. Her personality was more dog-like, so Danette felt she had the perfect combination to replace her recent losses. The first few weeks went well as the two checked each other out but after a couple of weeks Dolly's personality took a sharp turn. She began to stalk and attack Danette and hunt her down to the point of biting and breaking skin. Danette even needed to lock her outside the bedroom for fear she would attack her in her sleep.

Danette tried for some time to control Dolly's behavior and finally feared that she might need to have her declawed to help manage some of her aggression. Before taking this action, Danette decided to contact the UGA VTH to see if the Behavioral Medicine Service would be able to help. Danette and Dolly met with Dr. Dantas who diagnosed Dolly with arousal based aggression. Dr. Dantas determined that Dolly has a very strong predatory behavior and her needs were not being met.

Dr. Dantas recommended a number of behavior therapy techniques to help reduce Dolly's aggression. One was to use battery operated toys that have a lot of movement for Dolly to attack and chase. She was also able to teach Dolly that her blanket is her safe place. Now Dolly feels at peace in the privacy of her blanket – and so does Danette. Danette says that after five months she could see a huge improvement in Dolly's behavior. When Dolly plays, it is now controlled. Although she still plays hard, she gets her aggressive needs met in ways that have allowed both Danette and Dolly to build a bond of trust. Dolly stopped attacking because her behavioral and mental health needs were met and because she was taught alternative ways to interact with her owner.

Many people do not think of behavioral problems in pets as life threatening, but they certainly can be. More animals are returned to shelters or euthanized because the owners don't know how to deal with the animal's behavior than for any other reason. Just as with people, psychiatric treatment can be life saving. Danette says that the staff in the Behavioral Medicine Service has a great desire to help owners and pets live together and get along for the health and well being of both owner and pet. She says that she is a huge fan of these people who have helped her have the Dolly she always wanted. Dolly still has her claws, but now she isn't using them on Danette.

Name:
Winnie

Owners:
Andy Linn and family

ENGLISH BULLDOG
Age: 5
Address: ALPHARETTA, GA

Condition:
Pulmonary Stenosis

Winnie
the Dream Dog

Andy Linn had a dream. Literally. He pictured himself in his dream with a lost puppy, a white fluffy Bulldog with a big brown spot on her lower back. He told his wife and children about his dream over breakfast the next morning and his son and daughter became obsessed with finding the dog in their father's dream. They Googled Bulldog puppies until they found a litter that had a puppy matching Andy's "dream dog" description. When he saw it, Andy said, "That's the dog!" His children were ecstatic but Andy tried to intercede with all the rational reasons why getting a dog from a dream might not be a good idea. Finally, as most good husbands would do, he said, "Ask your mother." To the children's amazement, she said "yes." The search eventually took Andy to the breeder who told him about Winnie, the puppy he had seen on the website. The breeder lived out of state so Winnie had her first flying experience and was greeted at baggage claim by the entire Linn family. When the attendant opened the door of the crate, Winnie ran into their arms licking and kissing them. Her nubby tail would not stop wagging. It seems that Winnie had also had the same dream.

Winnie is a sweet and loving Bulldog with a heart of gold. Unfortunately, the Linns discovered that her heart also had a chronic condition when they took her to their local veterinarian the week after her arrival for her first checkup. From there, they were referred to the UGA VTH. Winnie saw the cardiology team and, after many tests, they were able to diagnose the cause of her heart murmur: stenosis of the pulmonic valve. This gave hope to the Linn family. At the age of one, she successfully underwent a balloon valvuloplasty, a procedure to widen her narrowed heart valve. In this procedure, a catheter is passed along a vein of the back leg all the away to the heart where the valve is located. The catheter has a small balloon at the tip. Once positioned across the valve, the balloon is inflated and the valve is stretched open relieving the obstruction. Winnie returned to her home and the family that had become so fond of this sweet girl.

Shortly before Winnie reached her second birthday, her heart valve narrowed again. Her amazing cardiology team was determined to find a solution and met with the Hospital's oncology team to explore the viability of treating Winnie with targeted radiation to help kill the tissue growing over her heart valve. They concluded that Winnie was a perfect match for this clinical trial. The Linns agreed to proceed. As several treatments were needed, the radiation oncology team created a body mold that was perfectly contoured to her body for targeted radiation.

Today, Winnie lives a full and happy life and recently celebrated her fifth birthday. Not only does the Linn family thank the faculty, staff, and students at the UGA VTH for their love, compassion and expertise, but for not giving up until they found a solution that worked for Winnie - a dream come true.

Name:
Nacho

Owners:
**Barbara Elliott
Marshall Elliott**

BOER GOAT
Age: **7**
Address: DAVISBORO, GA

Condition:
Broken leg

Nacho *Extra Spicy*

You can understand why a Boer goat named Nacho, whose favorite drink was Dr. Pepper and favorite food was a cheeseburger and who had a twin named Dorito, was pretty popular on the Elliott's farm. Nacho and Dorito were born on the goat farm and grew up with about 100 other goats who are shown and bred. Nacho quickly became a champion show goat who competed around the southeastern United States in American Dairy Goat Association (ADGA) and United States Boer Goat Association (USBGA) events.

In June 2011, Nacho was playing with some other billies on the farm when his leg was caught and broken between another bill's horns. When the Elliott's local veterinarians could not set the broken leg, they recommended that Barbara and Marshall take Nacho to the UGA VTH. Nacho was in severe pain so, not wanting to put Nacho alone in a big trailer, they loaded him into the back seat of their pickup truck, fastened the seatbelt around him, and headed to Athens.

Nacho had a severe tibial (shin bone) fracture. He had surgery and a large metallic rod, called an 8mm diameter interlocking nail, was used to stabilize his fracture. Following surgery, he spent a few weeks in the Large Animal Hospital recovering. Barbara says he was completely spoiled by the staff and faculty at the UGA VTH. Thanks to his time there, he not only healed well but also learned to love to eat fruit, and especially liked bananas and peaches.

Nacho returned home to a normal farm life and began to have offspring of his own. He was not only popular on the show circuit, he was also popular with the nannys. Barbara says that he has offspring all over the state! Barbara was a midwife to many of Nacho's offspring and she says that she gets calls from all the farmers around when it is time for an animal to deliver. She even gets an occasional call from the local veterinarian for advice.

Unlike many farm animals that are just part of a herd, Nacho thought he was a pet. When the grandchildren came to visit, Nacho would lie down and let them crawl all over him. Barbara also says that he was the best baby sitter she ever had. If any of the grand children got out of line or began to wander a little too far, Nacho would start hee-hawing until Barbara arrived.

Nacho was also an escape artist. He could always find a way to get the barn door opened. Barbara said she nicknamed Nacho Houdini because of his escape antics. During the ice storm of 2014, Nacho escaped from the warm barn and became stranded in the ice and Barbara and Marshall found him the next morning. While Nacho is gone, he still lives on with two great grandsons, Nubbers and Charley Boy, still on the Elliott farm and carrying on his tradition.

Name:
Cari Bradshaw

Owner:
Kathy Ann Holbrook

AUSTRALIAN SHEPHERD
Age: 10
Address: WILLIAMSON, GA

Condition:
Hemangiopericytoma

Cari Bradshaw
the Princess

Cari Bradshaw was a star. She was named for the actress who had the lead role in *Sex and the City*, Sara Jessica Parker, and she lived up to the character's role in the show. Cari's owner, Kathy Holbrook, knew from very early on that Cari was extra special. Cari was Kathy's tenth Aussie over a 30-year period, so she knew much about this breed of dog. Australian Shepherds are herding dogs and need a job. Cari's job was taking care of her mom, Kathy. Kathy retired when Cari was three years old, and the two were inseparable. After her retirement, Kathy began to take Cari for serious training. She was certified as an AKC Canine Good Citizen and, in 2011, she became a registered therapy dog. Cari and Kathy visited many hospitals, nursing homes and schools over the next three years and Cari knew just what to do to brighten up every person's day with her wardrobe of many different headbands.

In January 2013, Cari Bradshaw was diagnosed with a hemangiopericytoma on her upper right leg. Her local veterinarian performed a surgery to remove the cancer. After the lab results came back malignant, he immediately referred Kathy and Cari to the UGA VTH. For the next few weeks, Cari had 19 radiation treatments. Cari and Kathy had never before spent a night apart but Kathy says that everyone from the desk personnel all the way up to the faculty in Oncology made them both feel cared for and loved during what was a difficult time for both of them.

Cari returned home with Kathy and continued with her therapy work and her job of assisting and entertaining Kathy and all the friends who knew and loved her. She returned to the UGA VTH every three months for a follow-up with the Oncology department and, by all accounts, she was cancer free.

A month after Cari's tenth birthday, she became ill late one night and after a couple of hours she died peacefully in Kathy's arms from what may have been a heart attack. Kathy told me that she believes Cari chose a way to go that would be the easiest on her mom. I, too, believe our animals sometimes know what is best even before we do. Kathy also told me that if you said "I have a secret," Cari would put her ear up to your mouth. Well, Kathy, Cari just whispered a secret to me. She said to tell you she is having a grand time with all your past "children" across the rainbow bridge and that you were the best mother she could have ever asked for.

Name:
Duckworth

Owner:
Angela Nason

EXOTIC MUSTELIDS
DOMESTIC FERRET
Age: 5
Address: COLUMBUS, GA

Condition:
Pyothorax

Duckworth
Duckey the Ferret

Angela's husband was stationed at Ft. Benning, GA when she received a call from a neighbor who had found an abandoned kitten. Being an avid animal lover, Angela thought she would go to check out the situation and help find a home for the stray. It was one of the hottest days of the year and the "kitten" had climbed into the air conditioning unit to try and get cool. Angela took one look and said, "That isn't a kitten; it is a young ferret." Having had a number of ferrets over the years, she was immediately drawn to the young guy so she decided to foster him until she could find him a permanent home. She asked the neighbor if they had given him a name and the response was, "Duckworth, but we've been calling him Duckey for short." That was all it took for Angela to go from foster parent to foster failure. She told me that the minute she heard Duckey, she knew he was meant for her since both of her previous ferrets' names ended in ey......Oakley and Whiskey.

Shortly after Duckey arrived, Angela actually did find a stray cat. She named the cat Dova. Although she was concerned that the cat and ferret might not get along, the two immediately became fast friends playing and sleeping together. Angela says that even though Dova is much larger than Duckey, she had no idea of her size until one day she decided to stand up for herself. From that day forward, Dova was in charge. Nevertheless, they were inseparable. Angela is a paramedic and is often gone during the day so she leaves the two inside to entertain each other. She returned home one day to find Duckey unusually lethargic so she took him to the local veterinarian who immediately sent them to the UGA VTH. She left Duckey with the Zoological medicine service (called Zoo med for short) at the VTH and drove the 3 ½ hours back home to finish her shift.

Duckey was diagnosed with a pyothorax (a bacterial infection surrounding the lungs where the chest cavity fills with puss making it difficult to expand the lungs to breathe). The Zoo medicine doctors told Angela that she would need to decide quickly because they felt the longer they waited to intervene the less likely Duckey would survive. Angela didn't hesitate – her response was, "Do whatever it takes!" The Zoo med doctors anesthetized Duckey, placed a tube into each side of his chest to drain out the infection, and started him on antibiotic therapy. Duckey came through the surgery with flying colors, but he needed to remain in ICU until the infection no longer drained out of his chest tubes. He spent two weeks in ICU and two more at the hospital before he went home.

When Angela returned home with Duckey, Dora was so glad to see him that she treated him with the upmost respect and once again Duckey is in charge of this military household.

Name:
Princess Zan

Owner:
Anne Preston

QUARTER HORSE
Age: 18
Address: DECATUR, GA

Condition:
T-cell-rich large B-cell
lymphoma (Cancer of the
white blood cells)

Princess Zan

Zan came from a famous Quarter Horse lineage but, in 2009, her owner had a serious back injury and was no longer able to ride. She donated Zan to Stride Ahead, whose goal is to use horses to empower people throughout Georgia to achieve their highest potential. The staff mission is to provide transformative experiences in personal, social, educational, and physical development. There are three programs: 1) character building and life skills to improve academic performance and leadership for at-risk children, 2) therapy for people with physical and mental challenges and 3) programs addressing both the physical and emotional injuries of service men and women. When I visited Little Creek Farm, the amazing facility in Decatur, GA, I was extremely impressed with the staff and the work that they do. Stride Ahead wants their horses to love their work but not be overworked to exhaustion. Not only do these horses get chiropractic massages and trail rides, they also enjoy a two week vacation every year in the mountains of north Georgia.

Sometime after Zan's arrival, Anne Cumming Preston, the founder and Executive Director of Stride Ahead, took the horses to the mountains. A friend of hers who was undergoing cancer treatment asked to ride the gentlest horse available. That horse was Zan. As Anne's friend groomed Zan, she discovered a growth tucked up under her belly. Perhaps it was a miracle or perhaps it was Ann's friend's own cancer that provided her with a heightened awareness as most people would have surely overlooked it. It probably was a bit of both, but Anne's friend had found a cancer in Zan. The local veterinarian did a biopsy and Anne was informed that the growth was a malignant lymphoma (cancer of a type of white blood cells), and likely a very aggressive one. Anne was referred to the UGA VTH for Zan to undergo more tests and then surgery to remove the remainder of the cancer. This is not a simple procedure as surgical removal necessitated general anesthesia. The process of getting a horse anesthetized, put on its back, shaved, and prepped for surgery involves a padded stall with walls that move to squeeze and support the horse enabling it to be maneuvered and lifted onto a roller table. During surgery, the team found three cancerous masses: a skin mass, a lymph node, and a mammary gland. The Large animal surgery team assured the Stride Ahead staff that everything possible to treat Zan would be done. A week later, Zan returned to her stall and her herd-mates who greeted her with whinnies, knickers, and whickers.

In November 2016, four years from her initial diagnosis, Zan returned to her local veterinarian for her annual checkup and an ultrasound showed the cancer was back. They were able to perform the surgery locally to remove the cancer; the edges of the tissue removed (margins) did not contain cancer cells. Zan, once again returned to Little Creek Farm and the work that she loves - providing healing for the most vulnerable of people.

Name:
Atlas

Owners:
Gaye Chatov
Marc Chatov

GREAT DANE
Age: 10
Address: RUTLEDGE, GA

Condition:
Wobbler Syndrome
Osteosarcoma

Atlas *Bigger than Life*

Atlas was born in 2005 and came to live on their farm with Gaye and Marc in 2006. They knew very early on that Atlas was exceptional. And, oh my, did he have a personality! His favorite thing was laughter and he worked every day to put a smile on the face of everyone he came into contact with. Gaye says that when she was having a bad day Atlas worked even harder to make sure that her day was filled with laughter. Christmas was his favorite time of year and he was an expert at opening presents. This 165 pound giant would go from person to person to help them open their presents by first carefully removing the ribbon and then gently pulling out each piece of tissue. His joy came not from the gift but from the happiness it provided those opening the gift. Not only was he eager to please, he was eager to learn and went on to easily obtain his AKC Canine Good Citizen certificate – first in his class.

In April 2013, Atlas was diagnosed with osteosarcoma. The tumor was located on his front left leg. Gaye and Marc initially thought he had sprained his ankle but when the ankle became the size of a tennis ball they were referred to the UGA VTH. They were given two options. If they didn't remove the tumor Atlas' life expectancy was estimated to be only months. Alternatively, they could remove the left leg at the shoulder and follow up with chemotherapy.

With large dogs, more so than small ones, there is always the concern that being mobile on three legs might be a challenge. This was complicated even more with Atlas as he had been diagnosed earlier with a mild case of Wobbler's Syndrome – a disease of the cervical spine that can cause weakness and a wobbly gait. The Chatovs knew that if anyone could survive the treatment, it was Atlas.

Not only did Atlas survive, he went on to become the poster-child for giant breed dogs surviving bone cancer. He was home only 16 days when the Chatovs were shocked to see him running with their goats as he had always done. Atlas and Gaye became very involved in the organization Tripawds, which helps animals deal with life with three legs.

More than two years later Atlas, although 100% cancer free, began to show signs of his Wobbler's disease progressing and he died of complications from a stroke just short of his 10th birthday – a ripe old age for a giant breed dog. Gaye and Marc have no regrets and appreciate the additional time they were given thanks to the UGA Veterinary Teaching Hospital. With a spirit bigger than life, Atlas gave hope for large dog amputees. He lived every day of additional time he had been given to the fullest!

Name:
Miss Ellie Mae

Owners:
Stefannie Wilkes-Pounders
Micah Pounders

VIETNAMESE MINIATURE
POTBELLIED PIG
Age: 5
Address: COCHRAN, GA

Condition:
Intestinal obstruction,
spleen abscess

Miss Ellie Mae
Miss Piggy Diva

When Stefannie was a child visiting her grandparents on their farm, she found a piglet who had wandered over from a neighboring farm. She took the piglet to her grandparents who called their neighbor, knowing that their sow had recently given birth to a litter of piglets. The neighbors said that Stephanie, an animal lover from a young age, could keep the piglet. Her parents ultimately convinced her that raising a piglet that would eventually weigh well over 400 pounds would probably not be the best pet selection.

Stefannie never forgot the experience. When she was a senior in college, she began to research pet pigs and found a breeder of Vietnamese Miniature Potbellied Pigs in Strawberry Plains, TN. When she went to meet the newest litter, the runt immediately let Stefannie know that she was "the one." Stefannie took the piglet home when she was about six weeks old and named her Miss Ellie Mae. The first night, although Stefannie tried to go to sleep by herself in her own bed, this was clearly not going to happen. Miss Ellie Mae began to cry and the only way that Stefannie could get any sleep was to put this two-pound piglet in bed with her. Ellie snuggled her cold nose into the middle of the back of Stefannie's neck and both fell contently asleep. They slept that way every night until Stefannie married her husband, Micah.

At six months, Ellie became quite ill and Stefannie took her to the local veterinarian who gave her a shot for nausea. She was much worse the next day and they were referred to the UGA VTH two ½ hours away. She was checked in, examined, and given fluids. Through an ultrasound, she was diagnosed with an abscess on her spleen and Stefannie was told that her only chance of survival would be surgery. Even with the surgery, she would have only a 10% chance. After waiting such a long time for her dream pet, Stefannie chose to proceed with the surgery. Dr. Divers, the head of Zoological Medicine service at the Hospital, called with the news that the abscess had also been leaking toxic fluid into her abdomen and more extensive treatment was required, but Stefannie was determined to give Ellie every chance.

At five years old, Miss Ellie Mae weighs 60 pounds and is not only alive and well, she runs the household with Steffanie and Micah and their four dogs. Unlike most pigs, Ellie happens to be a picky eater but she is so smart that she can open the pantry door and pick out her own food. And yes, she is a Diva!

Name:
Annie the Pants

Owner:
Lizz Dorsey

PIT BULL TERRIER
Age: **7**
Address: ATLANTA, GA

Condition:
Intervertebral Disc Disease

Annie the Pants

Lizz is very familiar with Pit Bulls and has rescued a number of them over the years. They are amazing animals that often get a bad rap without basis. She heard about an animal in very bad shape at DeKalb County Animal Services. When she went to see about fostering her, she found her covered in mange with open sores all over her body. She knew that it would take from 30-45 days to get Annie into physical shape to be adopted. That was over four years ago. Another foster failure.

Annie got her name because she had no undercoat from her bout with mange and was susceptible to getting sunburned so Lizz found pants that protected Annie from the sun. Annie fit right in with Lizz's two other rescue dogs and her rescue cat. Lizz, who has had many pets, says that Annie is the happiest dog she has ever met. She likes to play hard – but also loves her naps. So you can imagine when Lizz got up one morning and Annie didn't want to get out of bed or eat. Lizz knew something was wrong. When Annie did get up, Lizz noticed that she was slow and wobbly, especially in her back legs. After visiting her local vet, who thought Annie might be suffering from a spinal cord injury, Lizz took her to a local emergency clinic. By that time, the weakness was much worse. Annie was suffering and unable to move her back legs so, after many hours of waiting for surgery, Lizz made the decision to call the UGA VTH. At 7 pm she and Annie headed to Athens. They were met by a team from orthopedic surgery and, after an MRI, Annie was diagnosed with intervertebral disc disease (IVDD.) IVDD in dogs is a common cause of back pain, rear limb paralysis, and an inability to walk or feel the back legs. Certain breeds, including American Staffordshire Terriers, are susceptible. Annie's condition was serious because of severe compression in her spinal cord and the paralysis was worsening quickly. Annie was in surgery for almost six hours.

After ten days at the UGA VTH, Annie returned to the home she loves and started on her rehabilitation. Lizz has done acupuncture and underwater treadmill therapy with Annie and ultimately had custom wheels made. Annie is a-typical. Her rear legs have spasticity, a condition where her muscles are continually contracted (they stick out in odd directions), so her legs don't fit as well in a wheelchair as if they were flaccid like most IVDD dogs. Lizz also takes her on "sling" walks where a sling under her belly lifts up the back legs allowing her to walk with only her front legs.

Lizz is in awe of the staff and team in orthopedic at the UGA VTH. She is sure if she had not made that call to them she would not have Annie the Pants today.

You can visit Annie on Facebook.
http://www.facebook.com/anniethepants

Anya *Diva Tiger*

Name:
Anya

Owner:
Riverbank Zoological Gardens

SIBERIAN TIGER
(ALSO CALLED AMUR TIGER)
Age: 1.5
Address: COLUMBIA, SC

Condition:
Subchondral Bone Cyst in the Distal femur

Anya was charming the visitors at the Riverbank Zoological Gardens when one of the them noticed that she was limping on her right rear leg and pointed it out to the attendants at the Zoo. The veterinarians at the Zoo treated her with rest and pain medication but, when the lameness continued for several months, Anya was referred to the UGA VTH. Further examination and x-rays isolated the problem to her right stifle (knee). Arthroscopy was performed to examine the structures of the knee but the lameness continued to be a puzzle. No apparent cause was found so Anya returned back home with continued pain medication treatment.

Despite the medication, Anya's lameness progressed and she returned to the UGA VTH for more diagnostic tests including a CT scan and an MRI of her knee. These tests found a large subchondral bone cyst which was expanding just above her knee in the femur (thigh bone). The cyst had been slowly growing over time but now was getting large enough to significantly damage the bone. Surgery was performed the same day as the CT and MRI. The bone cyst was removed and a bone graft was placed into the large defect in the bone.

Anya recovered well and within two months was back to her normal, playful, diva self. Since her surgery, Anya has grown into a beautiful adult tiger weighing in at close to 600 pounds.

In 2015, when the Racine Zoo lost their older female tiger, Niki, Riverbank Zoological Gardens donated Anya to the Racine Zoo. Today, at 11 years of age, she continues to charm the visitors. Upon arrival, the curator of animal care at the Racine Zoo said, "We've noticed that Anya demonstrates the same diva-like behavior as Niki. She has extremely long whiskers and loves the smell of Calvin Klein Obsession, just as Niki did. Maybe it's a tiger thing."

Anya has adjusted well to her move from the warm weather in South Carolina to the brutal winters in Wisconsin. The Siberian tiger originated in the Sikhote Alin mountain region of Russia so she is enjoying life outside in the cold weather like her ancestors did.

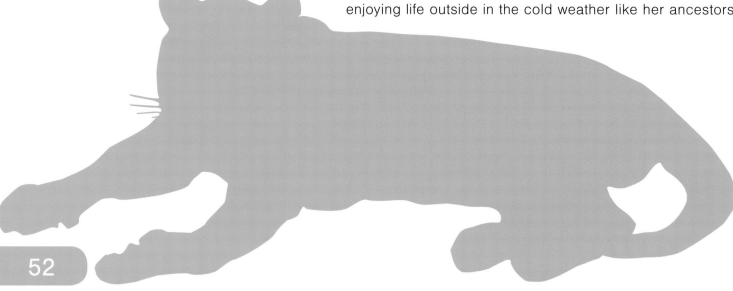

Name:
Buckwheat

Owners:
Stacey Faulkner
Todd Faulkner

MINIATURE DONKEY
Age: 11
Address: WATKINSVILLE, GA

Condition:
Severed ligament
and artery

Buckwheat
Miracle Donkey

Stacey and Todd Faulkner bought Buckwheat and his brother, Hershey, in 2005 as Christmas presents for their then young children. They chose to get two because, like many farm animals, donkeys do much better when they have another animal companion The miniature donkeys were so small at only a few months of age that Stacy and Todd were able to lift them and hide them without the children knowing. On Christmas morning, the children found directions to their gifts in the barn. What a perfect Christmas surprise.

Buckwheat suffered a life threatening hind-leg injury in September, 2006. The farrier was visiting the Faulkner farm to trim the horses' and donkeys' hooves and Buckwheat panicked. While trying to flee, his foot got caught in the barn door. We humans may find a manicure relaxing, but I don't know any animals that feel that way and securing them in this process is extremely important. As Buckwheat tried to free the leg, he severed a major ligament and artery in the pastern joint (a joint near the hoof). Stacey and Todd were told by the local veterinarian that, had he not been so small (and portable), they would've had to euthanize him on the farm. The Faulkners were referred to the UGA VTH where he was immediately taken to surgery. The surgeon gave him about a 5% chance of surviving due to the high risk of infection, lack of blood supply to the area, and severity of the injury. With each passing day Buckwheat improved, even after an infection. All of the doctors, students, and staff were pulling for Buckwheat as much as the Faulkner family and, after six weeks in the hospital, Buckwheat was able to come home. Recovering from such a serious accident is lengthy. Even after leaving the Teaching Hospital, Buckwheat required an additional six months of home treatment. His local veterinarian made house calls to continue to clean the healing wounds and change the bandages.

Stacy says that Buckwheat and Hershey are very sweet and happy donkeys but that Buckwheat has a bit more of an attitude than Hershey. But then, Buckwheat has been through a lot more as well. She says her favorite time with the two is when she takes a chair and good book to the pasture and they follow her and graze nearby while she reads. That is unless she hides treats in her pocket, in which case they chase her around the pasture until she surrenders the goods!

Thanks to the incredible care and support of the UGA VTH, at 11-years old Buckwheat has a long life ahead of him. He truly is the miracle donkey.

Name:
Duke

Owners:
Kimberly Earle
Steve Earle
Andrew Earle
Ansley Earle

BRITISH LABRADOR RETRIEVER
Age: 12.5
Address: ATLANTA, GA

Condition:
Peritonitis following GI surgery to remove a blockage

Duke
Christmas Eve Miracle

Two years after losing their beloved pet, Kimberly and Steve Earle decided it was time to bring another dog back into the family. Steve has long been an avid outdoorsman and a lover of waterfowling, so he connected with a British Labrador retriever breeder to look for a dog that would be as much a family dog as a sporting one. Thus, they were blessed with Duke, a beautiful fox red British Lab.

Duke is royalty from a bloodline of British Sporting Labs from Scotland. Fancy right? But he was still like any other Lab pup: full of energy and curiosity. He is always eager to learn and eager to please. Steve says that Duke has a true "On, Off" switch, and when he is "On" he is all business. On cold winter mornings afield, Duke could sit completely still for hours scanning the skies – much longer than his human hunting buddies. If Steve missed when he finally got a shot, Duke would look back at him with one of "those looks." When Duke was six years old, he earned the UKC title of Hunt Retriever Champion. He has traveled to many states to hunt with Steve but Steve says that, as much as Duke loves hunting, he always enjoys coming in after a day afield and curling up next to the Earle's son, Andrew.

The Earle's have two Labs and when Duke's "sister" developed a possible food allergy they changed dog food. The new food didn't agree with Duke and he started eating grass, as dogs sometimes do which often leads to vomiting. Duke didn't pass the grass and was taken to his veterinarian where he underwent surgery to remove a blockage in his gastrointestinal (GI) tract. All signs were that the surgery was a success but, 36 hours later, the Earle's could see that something wasn't right. Their local Emergency Clinic immediately referred them to the UGA VTH. The entire family went to Athens on a Sunday night with the Earle's daughter comforting Duke in his extreme distress. He was admitted to the VTH with a fever, high white blood cell count and, worst of all, an infection in his abdomen called peritonitis. The surgery doctors of the General surgery service operated and found that two areas of Duke's GI tract were leaking intestinal fluid into his abdomen causing life threatening peritonitis. The Earle family was in constant contact with the surgeon over the next several days as Duke recovered. On Christmas morning, they received a call to say that Duke was out of the woods. Best Christmas present ever!

Today, Duke is a healthy 12 ½ year old Lab. Even though his days sporting afield are past, he is still as content as ever being a dog who got a second chance thanks to the UGA VTH. Years ago, there was a popular song – The Duke of Earl. I'll never hear that song again without thinking of Duke Earle.

Name:
Elan Cavalia

Owner:
Caroline Mixon

ALPACA
Age: **7**
Address: FLOWERY BRANCH, GA

Condition:
Premature birth

Elan Cavalia
of the Count

Cavalia was born on a chilly day in December, 2009, one month early. She was not ill or underweight, just early. All the crias (baby alpacas) born to Carodel Farms have names that begin with "C" and while driving through Atlanta the month before the cria was to be born Caroline saw a big billboard announcing the horse show, *Cavalia*. She immediately decided on the soon to be born cria's name.

Shortly after her birth, Cavalia became lethargic and could not be stimulated to stand and nurse. Keota, the dam, knew something was wrong. Her pacing told her owners that things were not good. Caroline called her local veterinarian who said, "Transport her to UGA VTH immediately." He made all the preparations and the UGA team was waiting when they arrived about 45 minutes later. They went to work and saved Cavalia's life. Cavalia and Keota were at the VTH for a week until the cria could nurse on her own.

There is a fine balance in dealing with a lactating dam that has not yet bonded with her cria. The supply and demand of milk and nursing bond must be carefully fostered and developed. One must keep the dam milked out and the cria fed, plus transfuse the cria with plasma (the watery portion of the blood) to provide the cria with proper immunoglobulin (antibodies) levels to fight off infection. Three major things have to be quickly assessed: maternal response, the available colostrum (the milk that is produced in the first few days after birth that is rich in immunoglobulins), and body temperature regulation. Cavalia's dam was unable to provide all these things so, with much patience and understanding, the doctors and staff at the UGA VTH assisted both mother and cria.

The staff at the UGA VTH will always remember Cavalia and Keota, especially the senior veterinarian. As Caroline was about to warn her that Keota had an obsession with pulling ponytails, the dam made it clear that not even the veterinarian was to get between her and her baby. Keota grabbed the vet's long, blond ponytail and gave it a good yank!

UGA VTH has become a Mecca for camelid treatment. There are six living species of camelids (even-toed ungulated mammals), including certain camels, llamas and alpacas. Dr. Michelle Barton and the Large Animal Internal Medicine staff have taken their students and the UGA VTH program to coveted status among schools of veterinary medicine.

Cavalia returned home to her wonderful life on the farm and lived another six years. One afternoon last summer Caroline saw that Cavalia was not with the herd but was in the shade lying down. When she checked on her, she found a small .22 caliber bullet hole. Someone had shot this beautiful animal from the road and by the time Caroline found her, Cavalia was already septic (life threatening systemic infection). She died in Caroline's arms, the woman who had loved and cared for Cavalia from her first breath to her last.

Charley
Sweeter Than Apricot Brandy

Name:
Charley

Owners:
Jo Scheff
Pitt Scheff

APRICOT MINIATURE POODLE
Age: 4
Address: MILLEDGEVILLE, GA

Condition:
Herniated disc,
Degenerative disc disease

Joe and Pitt have always had pets, usually at least two. Shortly after losing their poodle, they received a call from their vet. An older woman had brought in a young poodle puppy and asked the veterinarian to help her find a home for him. The woman realized she did not have the energy it would take to raise and train a young dog. Charley came to live with the Pitts and their other pets.

When he was about three years old, the Scheffs observed that Charley's hind limbs were not working properly. They knew something was seriously wrong and took him to his regular veterinarian where X-rays of his back were taken. The vet thought that Charley's condition was most likely due to a herniated disc, so Charley was referred to the UGA VTH for confirmation, diagnosis and treatment.

The doctors at the VTH felt that, while some dogs with a herniated intervertebral disc can be treated with medication, Charley had a better chance of walking again with surgery. The MRI confirmed the diagnosis of a herniated intervertebral disc that had extruded into the vertebral column, compressing the spinal cord in the lumbar area. Charley underwent surgery to remove it. The important thing with this type of surgery is to keep the animal quiet and restrained during the recovery, usually for a four to six week period following surgery. Jo and Pitt took their instructions seriously and kept him in his crate with a nice padded bed except for his short time outside on a leash. After a few months – FREEDOM!

Charley continued to do well for some months until suddenly he screamed in pain. He was paralyzed in his back legs. He was rushed back to UGA VTH where he was found to have not only lost the ability to move his back legs but, most importantly, could not even feel them when a hemostat was used to squeeze his toe. Another MRI was performed which found another herniated intervertebral disc that was severely compressing his spinal cord. He had surgery to remove the compressing of his spinal cord by the herniated disc material. Given the severity of his neurologic signs, it was uncertain whether he would walk again despite surgery. Once again, Charley went home with instructions for strict kennel rest followed up with physical therapy. He is well remembered at UGA VTH running up and down the halls with his set of wheels while recovering from surgery

A year after the second surgery, I visited with Charley and his owners and he was walking on his own. So many rescue stories are a testament that the right owner ends up with the right rescue. This was definitely true with Charley and the Scheffs.

When I went to meet Charley in person, Pitt and Jo told me that their biggest concern was that Charley would outlive them and they wanted to be sure he had a good home. They said they were in their 80's, although I would have never known. I left wondering how old the "older" woman was that they rescued Charley from!

Name:
Image's Cherokee

Owner:
Dr. Heather Lindell

LEOPARD APPALOOSA
Age: 28
Address: ATHENS, GA

Condition:
Squamous Cell Carcinoma
of the eye, Splint fracture

Image's Cherokee
Team Cherry Superhero

Cherokee was born March 25, 1981 in Athens, Georgia. His given name was Image's Cherokee but most people knew him as Cherry. He began his show career in 1983 when he met his devoted partner, Heather Lindell, through Harold Hodgson, Jr., a pharmacist from Athens. After his daughter passed away from cancer, Harold donated a herd of her Appaloosas to the 4-H Foundation. One of them was Cherry.

The duo was formed when Heather was in Junior High. Cherry and Heather went to many horse shows throughout the southeast while Heather was in Junior High and High School. When Heather went away to the University of Georgia, Cherry went with her to get some higher learning. They BOTH joined the UGA Equestrian Team. Heather had to learn to ride a variety of horses and other riders had to learn to ride Cherry. He gave a lot of spirited rides to many of the equestrians. He was the superstar of *Team Cherry*. The riders still tell Heather their stories when they see her.

In 1996, Heather noticed uneven areas around Cherry's right eyelid while grooming him. She made an appointment for him with the ophthalmology service at the UGA Veterinary Teaching Hospital where he was diagnosed with squamous cell carcinoma (SCC). The SCC was located on his third eyelid. The third eyelid helps protect the eye and helps clear the eye of foreign material such as dirt and dust. Dr. Michelle Willis was the ophthalmologist on the case. Dr. Willis performed surgical excision of the third eyelid with follow up cryotherapy (a procedure where the tissue is destroyed by freezing it; this is done to kill any remaining cancer cells following surgery). Cherry did well post-surgery with no recurrence of the cancer.

Cherry was always an active horse and liked playing with his pasture-mates. In 2002, he was kicked by another horse and was brought to the UGA Veterinary Teaching Hospital for an evaluation. He was diagnosed with a fracture at the junction between the proximal and middle third of the fourth metatarsal bone. Since the fracture did not have any displaced fragments, Dr. Peroni, the large animal orthopedic surgeon, recommended conservative care. With stall rest and repeated follow ups with Doctors Peroni, Caldwell and Mueller, Cherry made a complete recovery and continued his show career.

Cherry continued to win many awards and accolades. He was a versatile horse showing in Western Horsemanship, Reining, Trail, Hunters, Jumpers, Eventing and Dressage. Thanks goes to the care given by the UGA ophthalmology service for maintaining his visual health, Dr. Lowder for maintaining his dental health, the LA Surgery team for monitoring his locomotion and the LA Internal Medicine and Ambulatory services for maintaining his overall health. They were all part of *Team Cherry*.

Name:
Riley

Owners:
Maggie Brown
Andrew Brown

DOBERMAN PINSCHER
Age: 5
Address: ATLANTA, GA

Condition:
Wobbler Syndrome

The Life of Riley

Maggie grew up in South Georgia and met her future husband when they were children. Andrew grew up in Atlanta, but his grandmother lived in Maggie's home town where he often visited. They remained friends throughout high school and their relationship even survived when Maggie left to attend college at the University of Georgia and Andrew stayed in Atlanta to attend Georgia Tech. They knew that they would marry, but decided to start by seeing how they would do with a pet first. They decided on a dog and Andrew convinced Maggie to get a Doberman Pinscher.

Riley was your typical rambunctious puppy, but learned quickly and became the dog both Maggie and Andrew had hoped for. His life was good until he turned two. In March of 2015, they began to notice that Riley was walking "funny." His normally beautiful athletic gait had disappeared and he was struggling to walk without losing his balance. Their veterinarian recommended they take Riley to the UGA VTH.

Within minutes of checking Riley into the emergency room, veterinarians rushed out to initiate the evaluation process. By the end of the day, a battery of tests had been performed to reach a final diagnosis of wobbler syndrome (aka Caudal Cervical Spondylomyelopathy), a disease that affects the vertebrae in the neck and causes compression of the spinal cord resulting in a weak and uncoordinated gait. It typically impacts large breed dogs, and most common among them is the Doberman Pinscher. The CT and MRI scans also showed that Riley had an overgrowth of bone compressing his spinal cord causing paralysis. The neurologist was confident that spinal surgery would be the most effective, if not only, treatment option. Given these findings and acute onset, surgical correction (laminectomy at C4-C5 on the right and C5-C6 on the left) was elected and performed on 4/3/15. Riley recovered smoothly from surgery and began physical therapy on 4/6/15.

He made major improvements each day and, at the time of discharge two weeks after entering the hospital, he was able sit, raise into a standing position, and walk with minimal assistance. Even though he was improving, Maggie and Andrew were informed that it was still a long road to full recovery.

Maggie and Andrew were able to take Riley home after 14 days with strict instructions for minimum activity for the next four weeks and gradually adding exercises to help with strength and coordination. Maggie says that those first few months was like watching a newborn baby learn everything all over again. Each day Riley improved and Maggie and Andrew gradually added short walks. Today Riley is totally back to his old self, chasing squirrels and ruling the roost.

Maggie and Andrew are so thankful to the UGA VTH for the quick diagnosis and the outstanding surgery and rehabilitation of their beloved Riley. I had a great visit with the three and you would never know that anything was ever wrong with this beautiful and graceful creature. Maggie and Andrew did so well taking care of Riley, they married in May of 2016, and are now a very well adjusted family of three.

Name:
Bye Holli Farm

Owners:
Lucy Byers
Andy Byers

Age: 7
Address: WARRENTON, GA

Condition:
Multiple Animal Injuries/
Illnesses

Bye Holli Farm

Lucy and Andy Byers' first experience with the UGA VTH occurred in 1998 when their two young daughters' registered Morgan horse, Nicky, had an episode of colic. The Byers had purchased her several months prior when she was in foal. Nicky's only hope was surgery, so the family sat all night at the UGA VTH. They were able to observe firsthand the surgery that saved Nicky's life. Nicky returned home several days later with strict instructions. She would need to be walked every two hours, 24 hours a day for seven days, then gradually weaned to two times a day for another month. The mare fully recovered from the surgery and, in the spring of 1999, delivered a healthy foal. Several years later she delivered another foal. Nicky lived to be 32 years old and both of her offspring remain on the farm to this day.

The Byers' next experience with the UGA VTH was in 2011, when Lucy's mother's sheltie/mix, Sandy, had acute liver failure and pancreatitis. The local vet immediately referred them to the emergency room at the UGA VTH where Sandy spent several days in ICU with little hope. Thanks to the excellent care he received, he fully recovered and is still a constant companion and "ears" for Lucy's 83 year old mother.

In 2011, Lucy inherited her family's 250 acre farm in Warrenton, Georgia. The farm had not been well maintained for some time. Lucy and Andy, now retired, knew that there would be much work to do but felt they needed to be good stewards of the land. The first step, after fencing five acres, was to purchase five cows to help with the cleanup process. While bidding at the private treaty sale, they realized that all the buyers were giving farm names so they hurriedly named their new farm Bye Holli Farm. That auction night, in February 2013, Bye Holli Farm was born. Bye for Byers and Holli for Lucy's maiden name, Holliman. Lucy got a little "paddle happy" and came home with 11 cows instead of five!

In 2014, Lucy noticed that one of the cows had a red, swollen, draining eye. Lucy and Andy realized this was more than just an injury. Their oldest daughter, now a swine veterinarian practicing in North Carolina, made a referral to the UGA VTH. Dr. Credille came to the farm to evaluate the situation. It was a pinkeye outbreak and treatment protocols were implemented immediately. The Byers were so impressed with Dr. Credille's knowledge and dedication they decided to have the production department help with guidance on their herd management. They feel that this relationship is one of the best decisions they have made in their cattle operation.

Thanks to the guidance of the UGA VTH Beef Production Team, Bye Holli Farm is thriving with over 70 head of cattle and various and sundry other animals. They continue to have a symbiotic relationship and look forward to continuing that relationship for many years to come.

Name:
Stella

Owners:
Nicole Zitron
Jeff Zitron

BOUVIER DES FLANDRES
Age: 8
Address: SANDY SPRINGS, GA

Condition:
Cancer of the nasal cavity,
Hemangiosarcoma

Stella Emory Hero

When the Zitrons lost their first dog, Kodiak, a Bouvier des Flandres, they were determined to try and find a replacement with another of this breed. Their search eventually led them to a breeder in Boulder, CO who had "puppies on the ground." The breeder had a 24-hour video cam on the puppies and the Zitrons were able to see them. They fell in love with Stella immediately, even before they knew she would be theirs. They flew to pick Stella up and this tiny puppy flew home with them and came off the airplane and into their hearts.

Nicole knew that Stella was special from an early age because of her stoic personality, eagerness to learn, and obsession with food. She was a perfect candidate for obedience and agility training and the two of them began going to classes when she was six months old. She received her Novice Agility Certification in record time. When Stella was five, she was selected to participate in a research program at Emory University using MRI to study how a dog's brain functions. Typically, MRI provides veterinarians with a picture of what the brain looks like. Is there an infection in the brain or a malformation or a cancer? To accomplish this, animals are anesthetized as they need to remain still for up to an hour. But this study was different. Researchers wanted to use MRI to see how the brain functioned, not what it looked like. In order to observe the brain functioning, the canine subject needed to be wide awake! To qualify for this program, the selected dogs had to be very good with both voice and hand commands and able to sit still for long periods of time without sedation. Stella was a star.

When Stella was eight years old, Nicole noticed a drop of blood on the end of her nose. Her local veterinarian said Stella would need an MRI to confirm her suspicion of a nasal cancer. Because of the research project at Emory, Stella was able to take advantage of the equipment available to her and had an MRI that showed a cancer in her nasal cavity. Stella was then referred to UGA VTH and she began a series of radiation treatments. The effects of the radiation on the tumor were followed with MRIs showing the shrinkage of the tumor. It was working! Dr. Nicole Northrup, from the UGA VTH Oncology Department and Emory University's Dr. Greg Berns collaborated on a joint project to document this first-time research (www.gregoryberns.com).

Stella did well for a number of months until she collapsed suddenly and was diagnosed with an aggressive hemangiosarcoma (a malignant cancer of blood vessels) in her abdomen. This time the prognosis was not good and a difficult decision had to be made. With her family by her side, tearful goodbyes were said and Stella journeyed over the Rainbow Bridge to meet Kodiak. I have seen our animals help us decide the right thing to do many times. The ever stoic Stella led an amazing life and the legacy of her research will help others in many ways, including assisting the US military in better identifying and training explosives detection and service dog candidates, as well as helping understand the canine brain for better training and behavior modification techniques.

Name:
Sophie

Owners:
**Becky Brazer
Mitch Brazer**

PERSIAN CAT
Age: 6
Address: LAWRENCEVILLE, GA

Condition:
Urination outside litter box
Interstitial cystitis

Sophie
UGA VTH Graduate

Becky and Mitch have always had two cats, a male and a female. After their last female cat died, their male, Max, became depressed and lonely so the Brazers decided to get another female to keep him company. Sophie arrived when she was eight weeks old and, although he was a bit unsure at first, Max eventually accepted Sophie but continued to be the assertive cat. As Max aged, Sophie eventually took over as the more assertive of the two. While Sophie was friendly and affectionate as a kitten, she became more independent as she matured. Becky had new job responsibilities that caused her to travel more often and their son was home from school on summer vacation so Sophie's routine was interrupted. After returning from a trip, Becky noticed there was a urine spot on her sofa. She assumed it was the aging Max. When she realized it was Sophie, she took her to her local veterinarian who recommended fluoxetine (generic form of Prozac) to alleviate what was thought to be inappropriate urination outside the litterbox induced by stress. Urination outside the litter box can sometimes be caused by a cats need to "mark" or urinate in inappropriate places in response to high levels of stress

For over a year, life was good. Becky gave Sophie her fluoxetine in a pill pocket and Sophie took it with no problem. After the year of thinking everything was fine, Sophie realized that there was something in the pill pocket that she didn't like and started refusing to take it. When Becky tried to administer the pill herself, Sophie became more stressed (as did Becky). Sophie returned to her pattern of urination outside the box, primarily on chairs and beds. After Max died, Becky and Mitch thought that replacing him with another male kitten would help but Sophie's behavior continued.

As a last resort, Becky took Sophie to Dr. Dantas in Behaviorial Medicine Service at the UGA VTH. Dr. Dantas believes there is a reason for every action in an animal and it is her job to help the owner find the reason. Dr. Dantas worked with Becky and Mitch to eliminate the stressors in Sophie's life. She gave them techniques, including teaching Sophie coping/self-calming methods and teaching her owners how to properly administer her medication (a big stressor to Sophie), to help resolve the problem. Becky says that, of everything she learned, proper "pilling" was one of the most helpful. Now, when it is time to give Sophie her fluoxetine, Sophie jumps on the counter and turns around with her back to Becky and Becky, from behind, opens Sophie's mouth from the sides with one hand and pops the pill in with the other.

Becky says that, not only did her son and daughter-in-law graduate from UGA, Sophie also graduated from the UGA VTH. Once the underlying anxiety and the cycle of pain and inflammation are treated, interstitial cystitis can go into remission and clinical signs such as urination outside of the litter box can be extinguished.

Name:
Rascal

Owners:
John Mazzola
Penny Mazzola

YORKSHIRE TERRIER
Age: **2**
Address: GRAY, GA

Condition:
Broken bones, ruptured
intestines from injury

My Little Rascal

John Mazzola and his dog, Rascal, are inseparable. Whether they are walking around town, going to softball games or riding in the car with a "1Rascal" license plate, they are always together. On one of their walks, Rascal was hit by a pick-up truck, right in front of John.

John rushed Rascal home and headed as fast as he could to their local veterinarian, where Penny met him. Their vet took one look and said they would not be able to do anything to save Rascal and if he was going to have any chance, they would have to rush him to the UGA VTH. With an IV attached, their son drove all three to the emergency entrance at UGA VTH where the team met them and rushed Rascal in for evaluation. Rascal had a broken pelvis, a hole in his abdominal wall, and a ruptured bladder. In addition, he had severe bruising to his lungs making it difficult for him to breathe. Rascal was put on a ventilator to help him breathe until they could get him stabilized for surgery. When he was stable enough, his body wall and bladder were repaired and two tiny screws were placed in his pelvis to realign the broken pieces, a surgery requiring the most delicate touch because of the small frame of this little 15 pound guy. Two days later, Rascal developed a fever, swelling around abdominal incision and a high white blood cell count. The biggest concern was not that the broken bones would not heal but that what might seem like a small infection could rapidly escalate to a life threatening systemic infection and Rascal still might not survive.

John and Penny were presented with the idea of using vacuum assisted wound closure to help Rascal. VAC is a technique where suction is applied to an open cell foam bandage. It not only helps clear infection from wounds but also helps speed up the process of healing. While UGA had utilized this technique on many occasions, the Hospital's current equipment used to create the vacuum was too large and cumbersome to use on Rascal. A prototype machine in use in California had had miraculous success so the team asked John and Penny what they thought. John says he didn't hesitate. He said, "Have it sent here!" The machine arrived and the dressing and VAC were applied to Rascal. His recovery was miraculous but, as John was getting ready to come take Rascal home, the doctor told John that Rascal had not been eating well and to bring his favorite foods. When John arrived with steak and grilled chicken he had freshly prepared, the doctor said: "No wonder he isn't eating our food!"

Penny and John still take Rascal back for visits where he runs up and down the halls looking for all his favorite staff and faculty to give kisses and thanks for all they did to keep him alive. John says that the team at UGA VTH is more than just about medical care. The care is what "fixes" our pets, but it is the love that heals our animals – Rascal got lots of both in Athens.

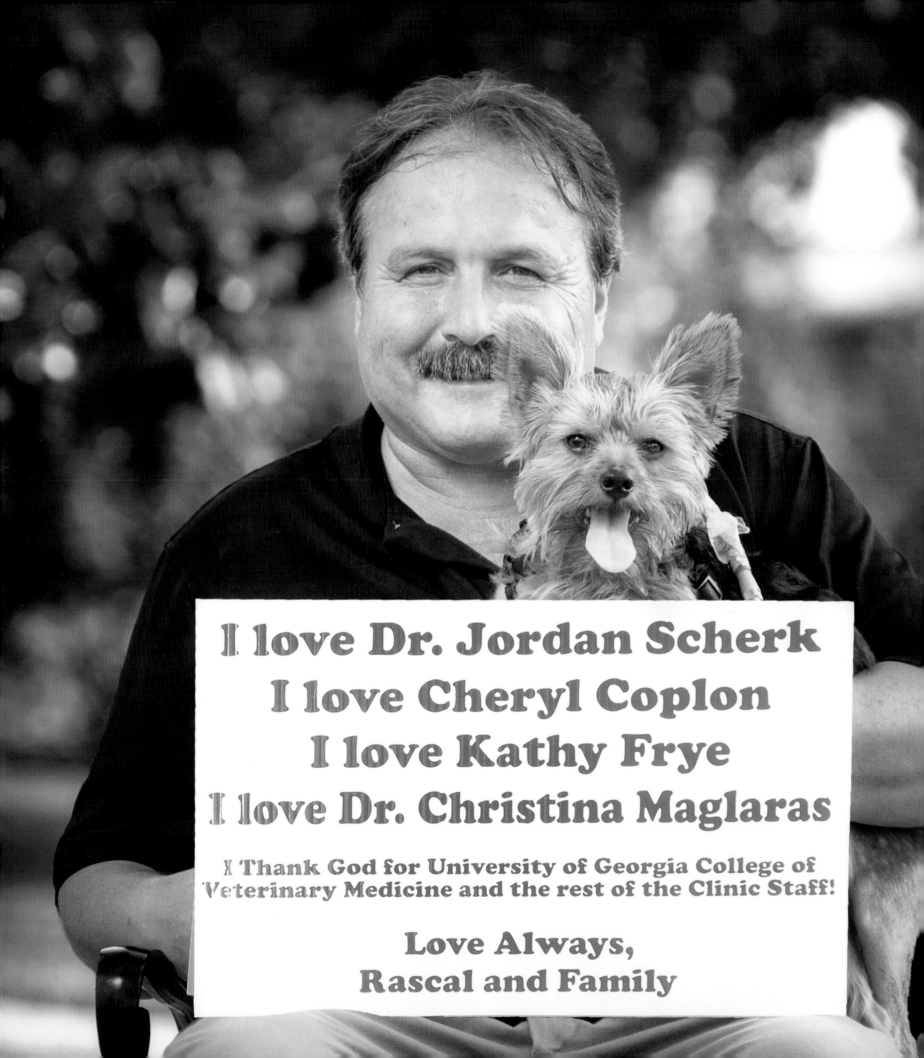

I love Dr. Jordan Scherk
I love Cheryl Coplon
I love Kathy Frye
I love Dr. Christina Maglaras

I Thank God for University of Georgia College of
Veterinary Medicine and the rest of the Clinic Staff!

Love Always,
Rascal and Family

Name:
Hot Rod

Owner:
Beth Nobles

QUARTER HORSE
Age: 11
Address: WARTHEN, GA

Condition:
Fall from moving trailer – multiple lacerations

Hot Rod
Escape Artist

Beth is an avid equestrian who at a young age, learned to ride on a neighbor's horse, Crown Royal. Beth and Crown had a special bond and after Beth married and moved away she continued to go back for visits. When her neighbor was diagnosed with a terminal illness, she called and asked Beth if she would take Crown Royal. As heart-broken as she was at losing her friend, her gain was having her favorite mare back. In addition, her neighbor also left her a young Quarter Horse – Hot Rod. Crown Royal lived to be 32 years of age and, when she was no longer able to be ridden, Beth and Hot Rod began to develop their own special bond.

Beth and Hot Rod, along with Beth's friend, were driving to a horse clinic one warm summer day when Beth realized that the trailer door had come open. Hot Rod was a seasoned traveler so you can imagine Beth's horror when she got out of the truck and saw Hot Rod's front legs, head and neck extended out of the door on a busy highway with traffic zooming by. His left hind hoof was caught in the divide of the stud compartment. Beth was able to slip a halter on his head and slowly ease the rest of his body onto the road. While still on the road Beth knelt on Hot Rod's neck to try and calm him and herself down and, by the grace of God, a large Mack truck stopped and blocked the traffic from making a bad situation worse.

Beth's friend dialed 911 and explained that they needed to reach the UGA VTH. Beth had graduated from UGA and knew the reputation of the UGA VTH. When the UGA VTH veterinarians and students arrived and came charging her way, Beth felt like her own personal UGA SWAT team had arrived. The true miracle here was not so much the extent of Hot Rod's injuries but the fact that quick action was taken to make sure that a bad situation was not made worse by either Hot Rod being hit by ongoing traffic or further injured by trying to flee.

Hot Rod suffered multiple lacerations on the face and neck and his heel bulb. Beth says that all who helped at the scene and at the Hospital were exceptional. As with all patients at the UGA VTH, the student assigned to Hot Rod called multiple times a day with updates on his condition and to be sure that all of Beth's questions were answered.

After four days, Hot Road was ready to go home. "Roddy" has no physical or mental scars from his highway adventure. Beth says that she gets a follow-up call every year from staff at the UGA VTH to check on him. Not only did they respond quickly and efficiently at the scene of the accident and at the Hospital, they continue to care long after Hot Rod's return home.

Name:
Isis

Owners:
**Kim Crutchfield
Mike Crutchfield**

DOMESTIC SHORTHAIR CAT
Age: 6
Address: BYRON, GA

Condition:
Multiple injuries and leg
and shoulder amputation

Isis Miracle Kitty

Isis was rescued from the local animal shelter when she was about six months old. She grew up on a farm and, like many farm pets, she was an indoor/outdoor cat. She was always ready to come in the house at dusk so the Crutchfields knew something was wrong when she failed to come in one evening. Mike found her hiding in the darkest corner under their deck. Kim says that when he brought Isis out her heart sank. Isis' leg was just dangling.

Kim rushed inside and called their local veterinarian who met them at his office. After reviewing the x-rays, he gave them two options: put her to sleep or take her to the UGA VTH. It was a three hour drive in the rain, but Kim drove while Mike held Isis in his lap to try and keep her comfortable. When they arrived at 11:00 pm, the staff took her straight in for evaluation. She was dehydrated, in shock, and in a lot of pain. Her left humerus (bone of the upper arm) was fractured and the elbow joint was luxated (dislocated). Her sternum was also broken but, most importantly, her lungs were severely bruised and air had leaked out of them (pneumothorax) causing them to collapse and making it hard for her to breathe. They arrived back home at 4:00 am in the rain with heavy hearts. Both the local veterinarian and the ER staff had given little hope for Isis.

The following day, the surgeon called and said that Isis had improved overnight after the emergency veterinarians had removed the air from around her lungs, given her intravenous fluids to rehydrate her, and given her pain medication, but they were keeping her in ICU because she was still a very sick kitty. Kim received daily calls updating her on Isis' condition. Everyone at the Vet School fell in love with Isis and her assigned student said that each time she walked past her cage someone had given her a new toy. She was one sweet cat, despite what she was going through.

Kim and Mike were told by the surgeon that her broken leg was so severely traumatized that even if it could be surgically repaired she might always have issues with it. So amputation it was. Amazingly, she was only in the hospital a week. Kim says that the worst part for Isis was the Elizabethan collar (E-collar) she had to wear. Once the collar was off, Isis was like a new kitty, only now an indoor kitty. My favorite story from Kim about Isis since becoming an indoor kitty is that, for the first time, she had to use a litter box. Initially, after trying to cover "her stuff" with her phantom leg she would turn around to find it still uncovered then look up with a "Darn, I missed again" expression. She quickly learned to balance on her back two legs and cover with her one front leg.

The staff at the UGA VTH said Isis was "one tough little cat" and dubbed her "the miracle kitty."

Name:
Kacie

Owners:
**Rick Marshman
Diana Marshman**

LABRADOR RETRIEVER
Age: 3
Address: PEACHTREE CORNERS, GA

Condition:
Bi-lateral hip dysplasia

Kacie Hippy Dog

Rick and Diana have always had Labrador retrievers. Their lab, Sandy is a certified therapy dog with Happy Tails, providing therapy to many children, hospitals and nursing homes. When Sandy turned nine, the Marshmans decided they would get a puppy that could learn from Sandy to also become a therapy dog. They named her Kacie. Labs are a popular breed of dog for this certification because of their gentle nature and eagerness to please.

Kacie was the classic energetic lab puppy but, after ten months, Rick noticed that she was limping on her back legs. He took her to his local veterinarian who referred him to the closest local emergency clinic where x-rays showed that Kacie had hip dysplasia in both hips. The emergency clinic was not equipped to do hip surgery so they referred Rick to the UGA VTH.

The Marshman's took Kacie to the orthopedic department for evaluation and the diagnosis of bilateral (both sides) hip dysplasia was confirmed with the lameness more severe in Kacie's left leg. The decision was made to perform surgery, a total hip replacement, on the more severely affected leg. They returned two weeks later and a cementless hip prosthesis (artificial hip) was implanted. Total hip replacements can be "cemented" in place or the prosthesis (artificial ball and socket joint) can be held in place by the healing bone that grows into the implant (cementless). Kacie went through the surgery like a champ and was released several days later with strict instructions. No activity for eight to twelve weeks and confinement in the house in a small room or crate. No running or jumping and no getting on the furniture. Try telling this to a one year old Labrador puppy! The VTH emphasized that it was imperative these instructions be followed. After twelve weeks, Kacie was allowed to start taking small walks on leash, gradually being able to increase the extent of time for her walks. This type of surgery requires six months to fully recover. At the time, Diana was also recovering from surgery so the two have a special bond from their six months of recovering together.

Kacie did very well for a few months but, once again, they noticed something had changed and Kacie was showing signs of lameness in her left leg. They returned to the UGA VTH where the exam showed a craniodorsal luxation of her left femoral head implant. The "ball" portion of the joint had popped out of the socket portion (dislocated) and needed to be repaired. Again, Kacie went through the surgery like a champ. She had to wear a collar for two weeks and then repeat the six months of recovery followed by both physical and water therapy. Today, she is able to walk and run normally. Eventually she may need the other hip replaced, but no time soon.

I had the opportunity to see this beautiful, well-adjusted lab with her sister, Sandy. Sandy, at thirteen years of age, is still performing therapy work with Happy Tails and Kacie is preparing to follow in her pawprints.

Name:
Nicholas

Owners:
Linda Ashmore
Rick Ashmore

HEREFORD BULL
Age: **6**
Address: GREER, SOUTH CAROLINA

Condition:
Intestinal blockage

Saint Nicholas

Linda has always had a thing for cows so as a Christmas surprise in December 2009, her husband came home with two young white-faced Herefords – Mistletoe and Holly. The Ashmores have a 22-acre farm and also lease another 90 acres where they grow hay and wheat. After getting the two young, shy Hereford's settled in, they gradually added to their herd with two more and then four more cattle. When a neighbors' bull escaped onto the Ashmore's property, a few more young calves suddenly appeared.

In December 2011, Nicholas and his twin sister, Noel, were born to one of Mistletoe and Holly's offspring. They were the first birth for their young mother. The mother was unable to nurture both calves so Nicholas searched the herd for six days to find a surrogate mother. His search was unsuccessful, so Linda and Rick took turns bottle-feeding him while he lived in their dog kennel. The Ashmore's six dogs did not know what to make of the young calf living in their home in the backyard. Nicholas thrived until March, when he developed serious bloat. After two days of being seen by local veterinarians, they were referred to the UGA VTH.

Upon arrival, the UGA veterinary team immediately went into action. After running numerous tests, it was determined that Nicholas had an intussusception (segment of the small intestine that telescopes into another segment) which would require corrective surgery. This surgery is most often performed on horses but the Large Animal Hospital thought it would be worthwhile to perform it on the young Nicholas. So he underwent abdominal surgery where the intussusception was resectioned and the intestines sutured back together. Three days after surgery, Nicholas was not showing any sign of improvement and the doctors determined that a stricture (blockage from scar tissues) had developed at the surgery site and a second surgery was required if Nicholas was to survive. The second surgery was successful and, after 14 days, Nicholas returned to his home in the backyard and the dog kennel. This was in the middle of the winter and Rick was worried that it would be too cold for Nicholas, so he installed a heater and even slept outside with Nicholas to make sure he was okay.

Today, weighing in at more than 1000 pounds, Nicholas is a thriving, happy calf, learning how to be a bull, not a dog like he first thought he was. Even in the herd, when he sees Linda or Rick he comes running to get his dog pat.

Linda and Rick are grateful for the talented, dedicated, and caring doctors and students at UGA VTH, and continue to stay in contact with these new-found friends as they all watch Nicholas grow!

Name:
Maisie

Owner:
Dean John Gittleman

YELLOW LABRADOR RETRIEVER
Age: 13
Address: ATHENS, GA

Condition:
Bilateral elbow dysplasia and mild bilateral hip dysplasia

Maisie
Vet School Mascot

John Gittleman is the Dean of the Ecology School at UGA and, when he is not in his office or teaching, you might look for him in his home-away-from-home, the UGA VTH. John is an avid animal lover and especially fond of yellow labs. He has had many over the years, but none more special than Maisie. Most of John's Labradors have visited the vet school for an illness or accident, but Maisie had a special relationship with the school and especially the hydrotherapy facility or, as John calls it, Maisie's Spa.

When John first got Maisie, he was teaching in Charlottesville, VA and commuting back and forth to New York City with Maisie. Even at a young age, Maisie was already a caregiver for John and pretty much anyone else who came into her life – human or animal. Maisie never had to be on a leash as she always knew where she was heading. She was never anxious and always determined to make the world a better place because she was in it. While in NYC, John took Maisie to a famous veterinary hospital, the Animal Medical Center. She was diagnosed with bilateral elbow dysplasia (abnormal development of both elbows that often leads to severe arthritis.) They were able to keep her comfortable with pain medication.

When John moved to Athens to become Dean of Ecology, he met Dr. Shelia Allen, Dean of the College of Veterinary Medicine. He told her about Maisie and Dean Allen suggested that hydrotherapy might loosen up ligaments and tendons, give Maisie more flexibility, build up muscle, and get a bit of fat off an old lab who had now perfected the art of sleeping all the time when John wasn't around. That introduction led to a regimen of "spa" visits once or twice a week for three years. When they drove to the hospital, Maisie and her "sister," jumped out of the car and followed John into the reception area. Then the dogs walked back to the hydrotherapy room as if they owned it and Maisie walked up the ramp and waited patiently for water to fill up to her chest. She happily walked in water for 20 minutes. Afterwards, she bolted out of the tub, got toweled off and walked as fast as she could through the gauntlet of students and vets, who at this point had become her cheering section and knew why she was there and how much the therapy had helped her. Occasionally a new student observed that there was a dog walking down the hallway with no leash. Eventually, someone would say, "Oh, that's Maisie, it's OK." During those three years, Maisie had over 360 hydro treatments with Dana Roller, one of the outstanding veterinary nurses at the VTH, unquestionably greatly extending both the quality and the duration of her amazing life.

The word 'mascot' originates from the French word 'mascotte' meaning lucky charm. Maisie was John's lucky charm and mascot to the veterinarians at UGA VTH, who work so hard every day to make our pets better. And the staff was better for having known Maisie.

Name:
Luke, Daisy & Bo

Owner:
Nancy Carll Kieffer

NEWBORN LAMBS
Age: 0
Address: CRABTREE, NC

Condition:
Premature Delivery

Luke, Daisy & Bo
Three Little Sheep

Nancy and Vic Kieffer were sheep farmers in the Asheville, North Carolina area. Their flock of about 100 ewes produced 150 to 200 lambs a year. The herd was protected by two llamas, Louie and Chewy and two herding Australian Shepards, Chris and Dusty. Over the past 25 years UGA VTH has been a "God send" to the Kieffer farm. Their animals were first cared for by Dr. Susan White and since then, by many other doctors, students and staff. She still uses a student she met at the hospital who now has a veterinary practice in Atlanta.

Nancy shared with me that one of her most memorable success stories at the UGA VTH was the delivery of triplet lambs, Luke, Daily and Bo, by cesarean section. During the lambing process, triplets were born prematurely from one of Nancy's best ewes, Bunny. Bunny had experienced a rupture of the tendon holding the ventral abdominal wall into her pelvis, a condition that usually results in the death of the ewe and often the lambs. She was also ill with pregnancy toxemia which affected the lambs as well. Surgery was performed at the UGA VTH to deliver the lambs and to repair the abdominal wall with a special mesh. The doctors treated Bunny's toxemia and attended to the sick lambs that stayed in the Neonatal Intensive Care Unit for several weeks.

Many young mother ewes have a difficult time with their first delivery and complications can occur and are compounded with each additional lamb. Often, with twins and triplets, the ewe is not able to sufficiently feed all the young lambs.

Nancy assumed the role of surrogate mother when lambs needed help being fed until they could feed on their own. Since Nancy was employed in Atlanta she and the lambs commuted to Atlanta during the week, returning to NC on the weekends. She said she would get the strangest looks when she would pull up to a red light and the baby lambs would stick their heads out the window. She would let them graze in her back yard in downtown Atlanta much to the delight of the neighborhood children who found every excuse to come over and pet the lambs. Bunny lived for many years on the farm with her twin sister Honey. Daisy, Luke and Bo grew up on the farm with Luke and Bo serving as herd sires.

Nancy still maintains the farm and continues to raise sheep, llamas and alpacas. She continues to commute with her baby lambs and two calico cats between North Carolina and Atlanta.

Name:
Lucy

Owners:
Elizabeth Cranmer
Tom Cranmer

GOLDENDOODLE
Age: 1.5
Address: LEXINGTON, SC

Condition:
Life threatening heart
murmur - PDA

I Love Lucy

After the Cranmers lost their dog, they decided to look at Goldendoodles. They visited a breeder with a red toy poodle sire and a white English Golden retriever dame and were immediately taken in by one pup. Weighing only six pounds, this little one already had an attitude and the Cranmers couldn't resist her personality. Meet Lucy. They brought Lucy home when she was seven weeks old but, after a few weeks, they noticed she was tiring easily. They thought that was normal for a young pup. When she was ten weeks old, they took her to a local veterinarian for her first shots. After her exam, the young vet took Lucy to the back to get another opinion. When she returned, she said she was sorry to tell them that Lucy had a heart murmur and explained she would die without surgery.

They contacted a local veterinary cardiologist and also contacted several other veterinary hospitals and decided to make an appointment with the General surgery service at the UGA VTH for a number of reasons: proximity, availability for immediate action, and costs. Elizabeth says she just remembers saying to Fran Cantrell who took the VTH call, "I need help!" One week later, Lucy was having surgery at the UGA VTH for a Patent Ductus Arteriosus. A PDA is a birth defect in the major blood vessel close to the heart caused by incomplete changes in the heart's circulation when a dog is born. In the uterus, the developing fetus gets its oxygen from its mother's blood stream. The ductus arteriosus is an important blood vessel that ensures that blood does not go to the lungs unnecessarily as the fetus is developing. As blood destined for the lungs leaves the heart, it is diverted by the ductus arteriosus back into circulation. During the first few hours after birth, this blood vessel naturally closes off allowing blood to travel normally through the lungs for oxygenation as the lungs begin to function when the puppy takes its first breath. In some puppies, the ductus arteriosus remains open (patent). This results in life-threatening changes in the way that the heart pumps blood through the heart and to the rest of the body. When the ductus ateriosus does not close naturally the dog can die from congestive heart failure and poor oxygenation.

At eleven weeks of age, Lucy went from getting her first vaccinations to a life-threatening diagnosis, to surgery. The goal of the surgery was to close off the patent ductus arteriosus. While the Cardiology service at the VTH can often do this procedure less invasively through cardiac catheterization, Lucy was not a candidate because she was so small. She had to have a thoracotomy (open chest surgery, where ribs have to be separated to gain access to the heart). Lucy came through the surgery with flying colors.

A year later, she remains healthy and happy thanks to her loving parents and the amazing staff and faculty at UGA VTH. Elizabeth and Tom are forever grateful to Fran for taking the initial call and directing them to all the doctors who refused to give up on Lucy.

Name:
Maxine

Owners:
Cathy Brown
Scott Brown

BOER GOAT
Age: 8
Address: WINTERVILLE, GA

Condition:
Severe bloat, kidney failure

Maxine
Maximum Appetite

When Cathy and Scott Brown (Cathy a veterinary pathologist and Scott a veterinary small animal internal medicine specialist – both focused on kidney disease at UGA VTH) bought a farm on the rural edges of Clarke County, they decided to raise Boer goats. They purchased a beautiful kid goat buck and named him Grancey. At the same time, they bought an Anatolian Shepherd, Sal, whose job was to be a livestock guardian dog. Grancey and Sal became fast buddies. Grancey and Sal soon had companions when the Browns obtained four more Boer does from a North Georgia farmer.

One of the does, Maxine, became their favorite. Maxine was an appropriate name as she had a maximum appetite. Any time a bucket appeared Maxine jostled for position to assure she had her "fair" share of the rations. The Browns goat herd gradually expanded and Maxine was a constant, as was her appetite. One day, goats being goats, Maxine broke out of her pasture and pushed open the barn door. Failing to find the source of her beloved grain, she climbed on the tractor and found a bag of Sal's dog chow which the Browns had thought they had safely secured. Maxine chewed opened the bag and, unfortunately, began to chow down. When they arrived home, Cathy and Scott found Maxine in the barn and quickly realized what she had done. Knowing that excess carbohydrates pose a problem for ruminants, like Boer goats, the Browns suspected they had a problem. They contacted the UGA Field Service team who confirmed their fears: she was in dire straits and her only hope was to be admitted to the UGA Large Animal Teaching Hospital. At the time of admission, her blood work was so dreadful that the admitting veterinarian felt it might be impossible for her to survive the night. She was suffering from severe bloat and kidney failure. The only hope was emergency surgery and intensive medical therapy. The Browns chose this course.

To the joy of Cathy and Scott, Maxine improved enough over the next few days that the large animal clinicians believed she might pull through. However, Maxine was anemic and the College did not have a caprine blood donor. Now it was Grancey's turn to help his friend. Cathy and Scott returned to their farm, loaded Grancey in a trailer and brought him to the College. He donated a unit of blood to Maxine. In hopes of making Maxine feel at home, they also kept Grancey in an adjacent stall as he received supplemental nutrients to help him recover from his donation. Over the next 10 days, Maxine gradually improved and both she and Grancey were able to return to their home and to the family they loved. Sal was part of the greeting party. Maxine gave birth to twin goat kids the following year and continued to eat with zeal, proof that she was back to normal.

The Browns believe it was the care for Maxine provided by the UGA Large Animal Hospital's dedicated team, skilled clinicians, and hard working staff that made the impossible happen.

Name:
Odee'O

Owner:
Diane Swain

WHITE POMERANIAN
Age: 9
Address: SIMPSONVILLE, SC

Condition:
3rd degree heart block,
pulmonary edema

Odee'O
Answered Prayers

Odee'O was six months old when he was given to Diane because his owners could no longer keep him due to a busy travel schedule. It was love at first sight! At seven months of age, however, Odee'O began having what his vet thought were seizures and the vet placed him on anticonvulsant medication. This helped for a year and Odee'O was eventually taken off the medicine.

A number of years later, Odee'O started exhibiting the same seizure-like episodes. Diane took him to her local veterinarian and, after looking at the results of the electrocardiogram (EKG), the vet diagnosed him with 3rd degree heart block. This is a conduction abnormality where the electrical impulses that result in contraction of the heart and pumping of the blood do not conduct through the heart. The end result is that the heart rate becomes so slow that the patient experiences syncope (fainting). As in Odee'O's case, it can be mistaken for a seizure. Eventually, it caused Odee'O to go into heart failure resulting in shortness of breath from pulmonary edema (fluid buildup within the lungs). Luckily for Odee'O, Diane worked in the field of cardiology as a cardiac sonographer so she knew immediately that the only thing that could save him was a pacemaker. After some research, Diane found that the UGA VTH was the best place to take Odee'O for the procedure. As soon as they entered the Hospital, they were greeted by a member of the cardiology team. He recorded Odee'O's history and took him to the back for evaluation. The team concurred with the diagnosis and recommendation for a pacemaker. It was also discovered that he had quite a bit of fluid in his lungs. The implant was scheduled for the morning and Odee'O was given Lasix (a diuretic) throughout the night to help decrease the fluid before going under anesthesia

Diane received a call before the surgery to let her know that Odee'O had a good night and they were taking him back for the procedure. Twenty minutes later the phone rang again and a voice said "Ms. Swain, I am so sorry, Odee'O has had a cardiac arrest on the OR table and we are in the middle of a code with him." Diane was devastated and heart-broken and could not stop crying. She prayed to God to perform a miracle. Ten minutes later, she received another call saying, "We got him back and we are proceeding with the pacemaker!"

Odee'O was taken into ICU after the procedure and placed on a ventilator for a few days. Once he was weaned off the ventilator, he went into an oxygen cage for another few days and was discharged after a week. This was just before Christmas and Diane says that it is the best Christmas present she has ever received.

Name:
Johnny Quapaw
and University of Georgia's
Golden Girl - GiGi

Owners:
Kay Moody
Bob Moody

AMERICAN QUARTER HORSE
Age: 20
Address: AIKEN, SC

Condition:
tie-back surgery

GOLDEN RETRIEVER MIX
Age: 11
Address: AIKEN, SC

Condition:
heart surgery, broken leg,
torn ACL

Johnny and GiGi
the Circle of Life

When Kay was young, her parents took her to the Blue Ridge Mountains. While her parents played golf, Kay rode horses. On one of their trips, Kay went high into the hills on an overnight camping trail ride with a group of young riders accompanied by a group of Cherokee Indian workers from Highlands Country Club. During the night, one of the weaker horses was attacked by a nursing female mountain lion and fatally wounded. The chaperones knew that the humane thing to do was to put her out of her misery. The children were heart-broken, but Kay, now in her late 70's, said it was one of her greatest learning moments. The Indians sat the children down around the campfire and explained that the nursing mountain lion was just trying to take care of her young and that they would not bury the horse but that the horse would provide nourishment for the next generation of animals. In other words, they taught these young riders about the "circle of life." The horse's soul would become part of the earth and provide sustenance to others. Later, Kay went into teaching science because of this story.

Kay continued to ride for years and, when her last horse died, Kay's veterinarian called to say that she had clients with a horse they could no longer keep. That horse was Johnny Quapaw and he was the family's young daughter, Nicole's, horse. When they brought Johnny to Kay, Nicole was 14 years old and, of course, quite sad at having to give her horse away. Kay made it clear to Nicole that she could visit anytime and Kay and Nicole built a life-long bond.

Six months later, while fox-hunting, Johnny began to wheeze and almost collapsed. Kay knew something was wrong and called her veterinarian who immediately sent her to UGA VTH. Kay called Nicole whose Mom then brought her to be there to watch the "tie-back" surgery that would open his larynx and help Johnny breathe. Kay says there were at least 18 people involved in the surgery. Afterwards, Johnny spent 10 days at the hospital with calls four times a day to Kay with updates.

Four months later, a friend of Kay's showed up with a young stray puppy. This lucky rescue would also have a number of experiences at the UGA VTH. Shortly after taking GiGi in, she was diagnosed with a heart murmur caused by a blood vessel that normally closes off at birth. In GiGi, it remained open and was causing blood to by-pass her lungs. Gigi had surgery to correct it, from which she recovered completely. While chasing a rabbit in the 2010 ice storm, she fell and tore her ACL (ligament in the knee). Back to UGA VTH for surgery! GiGi is now a totally healthy and happy 11-year old.

I had a wonderful visit with Kay and Bob and GiGi. Today, Kay is no longer able to ride and Johnny Quapaw is back with his original owner, Nicole. The circle of life continues.

Name:
Bubba

Owners:
Carol Duckworth
Laurie Eubanks

JACK RUSSELL TERRIER
Age: 15
Address: THOMSON, GA

Condition:
Stage 4b Lymphoma

Bubba
One Laid-back Jack

If you ever find an animal that needs rescuing, you need to know Carol and Laurie. Over the years, they have adopted numerous animals including, dogs, cats, horses, donkeys and burrows that were in need of a home. So you can imagine the relationship they have with their local veterinarian. These two had just lost their last dog when their vet called to say that she had a litter of kittens in need of hand feeding and would they help her out. While at the local vet office, picking up the kittens, a man came in with a very tiny newborn Jack Russell puppy. A local breeder had a new litter and didn't think the runt would make it so was going to kill the newborn by hitting him in the head with a brick. The man who brought the young pup in insisted that, instead, he would take the pup to the vet to be euthanized. As you might guess, the rest is history. Laurie left with the newborn kittens that needed to be fed and with the Jack Russell pup in need of a home – meet Bubba.

Bubba was not your typical Jack Russell. Carol says that he is the most laid back, cool dude you will ever meet. Of all the Bubba stories she told me, my favorite was when her great nieces and nephews were over visiting. She looked outside and they had Bubba dressed up in their clothes and the youngest niece, Katie, was in the process of flossing Bubba's teeth. He was just letting them do whatever they pleased and loving it.

When Bubba was about four years old, they realized that something was not right because Bubba was unable to stand up. After visiting their local vet, they were sent to the UGA VTH. Laurie held Bubba with an IV hanging from the truck mirror while Carol drove. After running tests, Bubba was diagnosed with stage 4 Lymphoma (a cancer of the white blood cells). He was in ICU for a week, to be followed by 25 weeks of chemotherapy. Bubba was a small Jack Russell, weighing only seven pounds, and did not tolerate the chemo well. He was very sick and unable to keep any food down, so the doctors worked extra hard to adjust the chemo to be effective while not making Bubba sick. He was finally able to complete the 25 treatments and went into remission and remained there for over two years. During a follow-up at UGA VTH, blood work showed that the cancer was back. The doctors worked hard to find a treatment that would be effective and, once again, this amazing guy started back on another 25 weeks of chemo. That was seven years ago.

Today, at 15, he is still in remission. Bubba may not be as fast as he was, but he is still loving life and the family who gave him a home instead of a brick to his head! He loves everyone and knows just how to draw out each person's heart, including mine.

Asa One Lucky Rescue

Name:
Asa

Owner:
Katie Beacham

MIXED BREED DOG
Age: 14
Address: ATLANTA, GA

Condition:
Hemangiosarcoma

Asa was adopted by Katie Beacham from the Athens-Clarke County Animal Control in 1999 when he was about a year old. He was hyper and bad-mannered, but eager to learn and endear himself to his new human. I knew that Asa was one lucky dog when Katie said that her priority as a young, single, working woman was to buy a house with a big back yard for her dog.

At the age of 12, Asa was diagnosed with Hemangiosarcoma, an aggressive, malignant tumor of blood vessel cells. Hemangiosarcoma can arise from any tissue where there are blood vessels, but usually it appears in the skin, heart, spleen or liver with the most common site being the spleen. The doctors at the UGA VTH knew that it was a long shot for an aging dog to survive this aggressive cancer and explained to Katie that surgery to remove the spleen, followed by chemotherapy, was the only option. Even then, Asa's survival odds were estimated to be less than six months. Katie didn't hesitate. Asa's spleen was removed and he visited the UGA VTH monthly for his chemo treatments. After surviving cancer for a year, Asa graduated to home chemo treatment administered by Katie. Asa tolerated his treatment well but, after almost two years, he developed side effects that were impacting his kidneys. The joint decision by his doctors and Katie was to take Asa off his chemotherapy to give his kidneys a break. Katie created a website, asahascancer, that followed Asa's journey and provided details of his amazing spirit. Without the steady dose of chemo, the cancer returned and Asa died just weeks short of his 14th birthday – totally beating the odds and giving him an additional two years after his diagnosis.

I'd like to end Asa's story with a quote from Katie's blog:

But realizing today that cancer isn't fair or preventable and that it often isn't easy to diagnose, was eye opening for me. I just now realized I wasn't a bad mother for not seeing the signs earlier. I didn't fail my dog by not recognizing he was sick until he collapsed in my kitchen. And it wouldn't have made me an evil person if I couldn't afford (financially or emotionally) to go forward. While medical philosophy regarding humans seems to be focused on keeping someone alive at all costs, veterinary medicine seems to consider comfort, quality of life, and other factors when deciding treatment or non-treatment for our beloved animals. Does that mean we have the option to take the easy way out with our animals, or does it mean we can evaluate a holistic set of needs when deciding how to handle a bad diagnosis?

So well said. I think we can all relate to the tough decisions we face when our beloved pets are diagnosed with life threatening illnesses. Thank you, Katie, for sharing Asa's story. Many will benefit from your wise words.

Name:
Lola and My Addiction

Owner:
Sarah Gottschalk

HANNOVERIAN
Age: 19
Address: BUFORD, GA

Condition:
Hemoabdomen

HANNOVERIAN / HOLSTEINER
Age: 2
Address: BUFORD, GA

Condition:
Hemoabdomen

Lola and My Addiction

Sarah has always had a love for horses and began riding a pony when she was five years old. She graduated to larger horses over time and rode both Western and English style saddles. As she grew older, her father thought she would outgrow the "horse" fascination stage and informed her that he could no longer afford her expensive horse addiction. That did not deter Sarah so she began work after school and on the weekends to fund her riding and jumping.

Sarah began leasing a horse her freshman year in High School and took that horse, Lola, with her when she started college at UGA. After two years, the owners of the horse informed Sarah that they were going to sell Lola. Devastated, she took out her life's savings and Lola became her very own horse.

Knowing that Lola was aging, Sarah decided to breed Lola when she was 14 years old. A few weeks before Lola was to foal, Sarah found her in dire straits. She was throwing herself down on the ground in severe pain. Sarah checked out her gums and found that they were ghostly white. She called her veterinarian who made arrangements for Sarah to rush Lola to the UGA VTH. Lola could not have been in better hands and was one of the first patients at the newly opened hospital. She was diagnosed with a hemoabdomen (bleeding into the abdomen) as a result of a tear in the ligament that supports the uterus which had also torn in the major artery supplying blood to the uterus. She was hemorrhaging and would require an immediate blood transfusion. The veterinarian told her that things did not look good and that Sarah needed to quickly decide her priority - save the mother or the foal. As much as Sarah was looking forward to the next generation of Lola, she didn't hesitate. "Save the mother!" The veterinary team performed multiple blood transfusions, seven liters of blood and a medication to help enable a blood clot to stop the bleeding. It worked! The Large animal vets informed Sarah that when Lola was ready to foal, she would most likely hemorrhage again. They jointly decided to keep Lola at the hospital with no assurance either would survive.

Not only did Lola's foal make it, she was the first birth in the newly opened UGA VTH. When her father understood that Sarah's love for horses was not a phase, but a lifelong dream come true, he said, "Well if you are going to have an addiction, I'd rather it be a horse than drugs." Sara named the foal My Addiction or Addie for short. Addie had a rough 24 hours, but was soon up and feeding on her own.

Today, Lola is helping young girls learn to ride and Addie is as sassy as can be. Sarah is riding her every chance she gets – when she is not planning her wedding on the farm where she will live with her husband and horse family.

Name:
Belker

Owners:
**Jayne Getsinger
Kevin Getsinger**

BOXER

Age: 14

Address: SHOAL CREEK, AL

Condition:
Collapsed lung
Torn leg ligaments

Belker
Loyal Tennessee Volunteer Legend

Kevin Getsinger's first job after graduating from the University of Tennessee was with Yellow Freight System. After working in Charlotte and Chattanooga, Kevin was transferred to Kansas City where he met his future wife, Jayne. After marrying in May of 1982, Kevin and Jayne were transferred to Athens GA the following winter. They decided to get a Boxer puppy as their first "child" and they named him Belker after a character on *Hill Street Blues*, Mick Belker, who was known for his gruff growl when dealing with criminals. Having grown up with Boxers, I can understand why the name would fit. They are gentle giants that love to play and growl!

Yellow Freight had a number of season tickets to UGA football games. Kevin was able to keep half for himself and his customers and the balance for surrounding locations. Shortly before the season opener with Clemson, just coming off a National Championship, Kevin received his tickets. Needing to decide which to keep for themselves, Kevin, Jayne and Belker went to an empty Sanford Stadium to scope out the seating. They were in the lower level of the horseshoe heading up to the concourse when Belker, being a young puppy, decided to run up the stands and jump the concrete wall landing 30-40 feet below on E. Campus Road. Amazingly, Belker survived and staggered to his feet. Kevin ran back to the main entrance and got to Belker and he and Jayne rushed him to the UGA VTH where it was determined that he had a collapsed lung and torn ligaments on his right front leg.

No one, including the doctors treating Belker, could believe he survived the fall. They placed a tube in his chest to inflate his lungs and put a splint and wrap on his right front leg. Kevin says that the staff was exceptional. During Belker's stay in the hospital, he was treated like a rock star. Everyone wanted to see the dog that flew out of Sanford Stadium. The inside joke was that when Belker, being a UT dog, realized he was in Sanford Stadium "between the hedges," he knew he had to get out no matter the eventual outcome. Belker fully recovered and went on to live a long and full life to the age of 14. This story happened over 30 years ago and many of the staff at UGA VTH still know the story of Belker, the University of Tennessee dog. A few weeks after the accident at the UGA season opening game, a stadium policeman said in passing to Kevin, sitting in his same seats, that a very famous UT dog had jumped over the wall nearby and survived. Belker was and still is a legend in Athens.

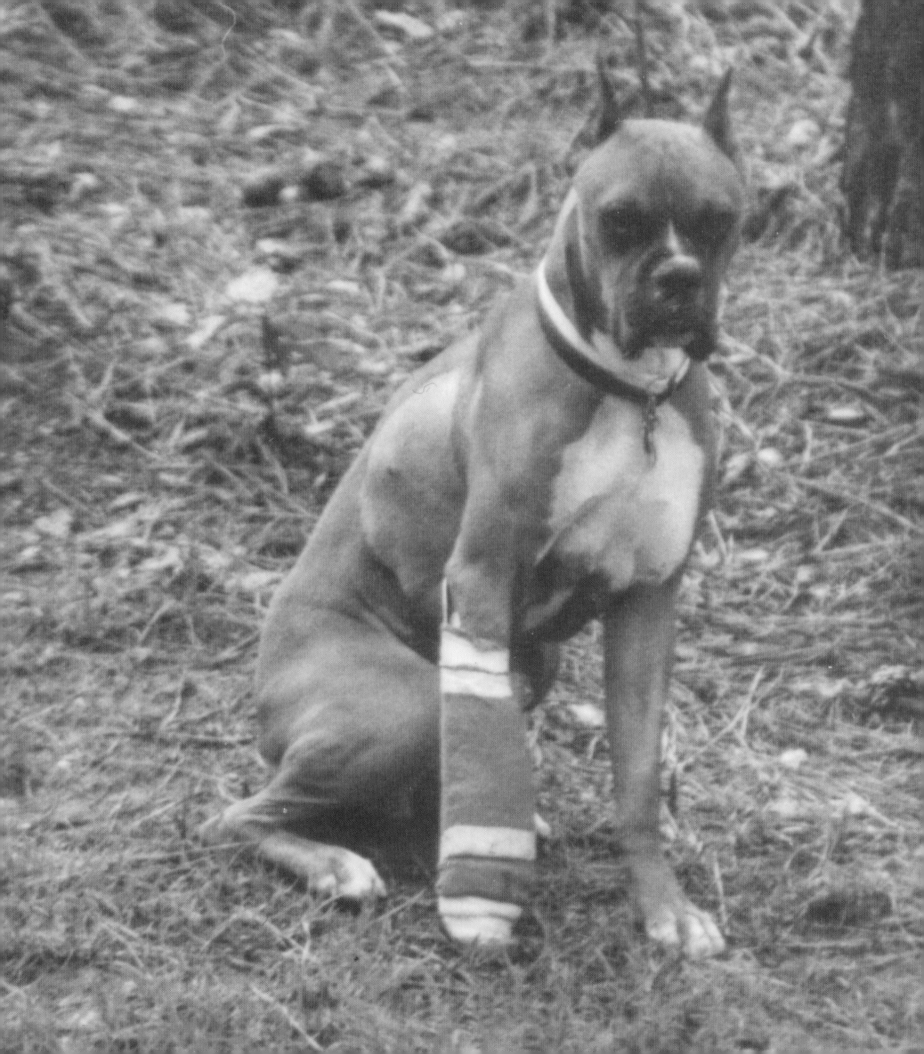

Name:
Bear

Owners:
Connor Smith
Perry Smith

LAB MIX
Age: 8
Address: AUGUSTA, GA

Condition:
Thymoma Tumors

Bear the Wonderdog

Bear, his brother and his mother were found abandoned on the side of a road near the Atlanta airport. The puppies were so small that their eyes had not yet opened. A kind man stopped his truck and picked them all up.

Connor and Perry Smith had recently lost their faithful old dog and were encouraged by friends to adopt one of the puppies. Connor knew immediately that the puppy would be called Bear because this bundle of joy looked just like a small teddy bear. With his web feet and love for swimming, chasing and returning tennis balls, Bear soon captured their hearts.

The first few years with Bear were pure joy, until his appetite decreased radically. Bear was diagnosed with hypercalcemia (high calcium levels in the blood) by his local veterinarian, who recommended that Bear be taken to the UGA VTH for a full medical workup. A large thymoma (cancer of the thymus gland) was spotted in Bear's chest cavity after many tests, and major surgery was required to remove the tumor, followed by chemotherapy and radiation. All seemed fine for a few months, but follow-up tests detected another tumor. This led to a decision for Bear to undergo another major operation so, once again, his chest was opened and more tumors were removed. Perry says that on his many visits to the UGA Teaching Hospital, Bear always entered with great joy. Somehow, he seemed to know that the kind folks there would take good care of him and they did not disappoint.

Bear – what a perfect name for this very resilient dog as bears are hard animals to bring down! Today, at the age of six, Bear has fully recovered and is doing well. Perry says he is the official greeter at their front door. If a robber should ever appear he would be overwhelmed by this 78 pound bundle of energy and joy.

Bear, the wonderdog, has many amazing talents like opening doors with his nose and telling time without a watch (he is always ready for breakfast at 7 am on the dot), but his most notable accomplishment is never wanting to run away. He knows exactly who rescued him and gave him the best and most secure life any dog could ever ask for. Why would he ever want to leave the people who saved his life?

Conner and Perry say the fact that Bear has survived two major operations plus radiation and chemotherapy in such a short period of time is truly a miracle. Thank you for sharing Bear's warm and encouraging story. I can see why this special guy is such a joy in your life. And you in his.

Name:
Archie

Owners:
Caroline Thompson
Drew Thompson

BOSTON TERRIER
Age: 10
Address: BROOKHAVEN, GA

Condition:
Immune Mediated
Thrombocytopenia

Archie
White and Black and Blue

Caroline's mom has a black-with-a little-white Boston terrier, Roxy, that is dear to the entire family. Caroline told her mom she would love to have a white one with a little black – polar opposite to Roxy. One day while grocery shopping, Caroline's mom and her husband found the dog of Caroline's dream for sale in front of the store. They brought the dog back to Caroline and it was love at first sight. She named the dog Archie for her alma mater, Ole Miss' Archie Manning. After a little work on general manners around the house, Archie began going with them on weekend trips to their family cattle farm outside of Athens, to deer camp with the guys, on canoeing trips down the Chattahoochee, and camping at the lake. He stands out in a crowd, and knows it. He has the run of the house with his lab "sister," Ellie, while Caroline and Drew are at work. When he isn't sitting on the back of the couch watching for their cars to pull in the driveway, he can be found sleeping in the same bed as Ellie.

When Archie was eight years old, they noticed that he was getting increasingly lethargic and developing large black and blue bruised areas all over his abdomen. After noticing his bruising, which started in a small patch and soon took over his entire abdominal area, Caroline came home to check on him and found he had spit up blood all over the house. She frantically took him to their local vet and he was immediately put on IV's and closely monitored. The vet called and said he needed to go to a more advanced facility for treatment. The Thompsons left work and took him to UGA VTH. The minute they arrived, an entire team welcomed them and assured them that Archie was in good hands. From that minute forward they were constantly updated and felt very encouraged with their doctors. Archie was diagnosed with immune mediated thrombocytopenia, a condition in which the immune system targets and destroys the body's platelets. Archie's platelets were around 10,000 with the normal range typically 250,000-350,000. While at UGA VTH, there were many highs and lows but, in the end, Archie spent nine days in the ICU, received four blood transfusions, and around the clock care from some of the best doctors and most caring students in the country.

Caroline and Drew brought him home Valentine's day, 2015 and, over the course of several months and much medication, Archie returned to the same feisty terrier that he had been prior to his illness. He has had two flare-ups since the big one but, thanks to UGA VTH and the Thompson's education of his disease, they have been able to catch them early and stop them. Caroline welcomed a son, Andrew, into their lives in October of 2015 and now Andrew and Archie are inseparable.

Name:
Mac

Owners:
**Lisa Alexander
David Alexander**

VEILED CHAMELEON
Age: 4
Address: CUMMING, GA

Condition:
Multiple head infections, dangerously high calcium levels

Mac *Allergy Free*

Lisa and David had long been avid animal lovers but David also suffered for years with sinus problems and allergies. Sadly, testing showed that the two things David was most highly allergic to were dogs and cats. While investigating alternative pets, the reptile family came up as an option to animals of the furry kind. Never having had a reptile, they began to research the availability and care of this kind of a pet. They attended the Gwinnett County Fairgrounds on July 2013 to look at the available reptiles and to get a sense of what might be right for them. Although they had no intention of purchasing that day, they came to a booth with a cage of newborn chameleons and the runt let them know that he was ready to head home with them right away! On the drive home, they tossed around names and, being avid Steve Jobs/Apple fans, they decided on MacIntosh – Mac for short. Mac was only about 2 inches long then and he rode home on Lisa's knee.

Mac began to develop some balance and coordination issues after his first year with Lisa and David. The first veterinarian they saw said that Mac should outgrow the problem, but instead he became lethargic and bloated. They were referred to another veterinarian who medicated Mac to help with his digestion. After several months, Mac was still not better and had also developed a head tilt (holding his head as if listening to the ground). David decided that it was time to take Mac to the UGA VTH. Dr. Mayer, responsible for reptiles at the Hospital, thought that Mac looked good and strong given that many of the chameleons he sees do not get proper care and, in many cases, by the time they get to him it is too late. The first thing he did was to take Mac off the medication he had been on which immediately improved his condition and eliminated the head tilt.

A few months later, Lisa and David discovered a bump on Mac's head above his right eye. Back to UGA VTH where it was diagnosed as an infection which was then drained and sent out for a culture. Blood work was also done and his calcium level came back dangerously high. They were issued strict orders for no supplements and no UVB lighting until his calcium levels became normal.

As he was improving from the head infection, he had another issue. The bone that connects with the tongue to allow chameleons to catch food was out of alignment. "This little guy just couldn't get a break," says David. Hand feeding Mac is a small price to pay, however, for the joy he brings Lisa and David. He spends much time just hanging outside his cage with them, seeming to think he is human. Like any other beloved pet, Mac enjoys just being with the family he loves.

Name:
Delsin

Owner:
Amanda Cook

CATAHOULA MIX
Age: 3
Address: ALTO, GA

Condition:
Septic abdomen, enlarged spleen, liver abscess

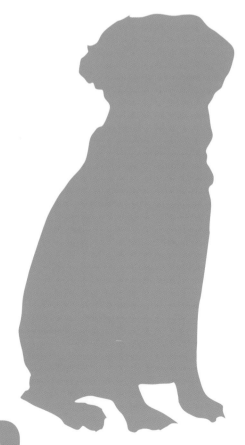

Delsin

Amanda and her brother, Bryan, grew up in the country on their grandparent's cattle farm. They lived on a road famous for attracting stray dogs – many of which had been taken in by the Cook family. One day in 2013, a dog wandered onto the farm and they soon realized that she was getting ready to have puppies. A few weeks later, they went from one rescue to six. This was a wonderful experience for the young teenagers who had only had grown dogs. They were able to see the mother naturally care for, feed and groom the litter of five. It seemed that the mother may have had an active sex life, since none of the puppies looked alike and, over the course of weaning the puppies, it was also clear that each had its own unique personality. The largest of the litter they named Delsin and, because he was a laid-back pup, they decided he needed to be Amanda's dog. Amanda's younger brother picked out Bear to be his dog. The Cook family knew they couldn't take on all, so homes were found for the mother and other puppies.

Delsin grew into an avid hunter. He experienced the wonderful world of wildlife and the family often found remnants of small animals that had provided a meal. One of those times, they noticed that his stomach had become greatly extended but, after a few days, all seemed fine. A few months later, the same thing happened and they assumed that another rabbit had become Delsin's evening meal. This time he didn't snap back. Delsin loves food so, when he wouldn't eat for days, Amanda knew something was wrong. He was also hot and panting, his gums were almost white, and his tongue was purple. Amanda and her dad took Delsin to their local veterinarian, who was concerned that he might have either a ruptured spleen or a cancer within his abdomen. Their choices were to put him down or go to UGA VTH. They weren't sure that Delsin would survive the trip to UGA. When they arrived, the staff took him in on a stretcher. He had so much fluid in his abdomen that the x-rays couldn't determine the initial cause of the distress, so they performed an ultrasound and found that he had an enlarged spleen and blocked intestinal tract. His initial examination revealed a severe infection in his abdomen. He had two liters of fluid that contained bacteria within it. What made it worse was that the infection had become a systemic infection called sepsis. Delsin's prognosis was grave and he needed emergency abdominal surgery. The Cooks drove home at midnight with a heavy heart. Delsin went into surgery at 1 am. Once the veterinarians performing his emergency surgery were inside his abdomen, they found that Delsin had a severe infection involving his liver. The surgeons had to remove large portions of his liver and also removed his gallbladder. Delsin survived surgery but developed kidney failure as a result of the sepsis. He spent 10 days in the ICU and another two weeks in the hospital's general ward to assure that his kidney function returned to normal, the fluid in his abdomen did not return, and that he was healing from surgery. Delsin arrived home in time for the holidays, wearing an E-collar and after four months is back to his old self chasing cattle and loving his mom.

Name:
Tyler

Owner:
Sara J. Dunn

POMERANIAN
Age: 11
Address: ATHENS, GA

Condition:
Immune Mediated
Meningomyelitis

My Ty

Eager to experience life with a constant companion, Sara researched rescue organizations and found a beautiful Pomeranian puppy at petfinder.com. She adopted Ty, an 11 week old puppy weighing in at a whopping 2.8 pounds. A few weeks previously, Ty had been purchased at a flea market but, soon after, a neighbor reported sightings of the family abusing the tiny puppy and he was removed by animal control and placed into rescue where Sara found him.

Ty was the perfect dog for Sara and they instantly bonded in unconditional love. A few years later, a "brother," Valentino, was added to the family. In March, 2012, Ty and Val went for their annual exam and everything was perfect until a few weeks after their exam when Ty began experiencing neck and joint pain, loss of appetite, and a severe limp. Additional visits to his regular vet did not produce a diagnosis.

Upon his referral to the UGA VTH, Ty and Sara were greeted by the staff who took Ty in for further evaluation. After an MRI revealed edema (swelling) in his cervical (neck) spinal cord, a spinal tap was ordered and a diagnosis was made: meningomyelitis. Meningitis is the medical term for inflammation of the membranes that cover the brain and spinal cord. The suffix (-myelitis) means inflammation of the spinal cord. Meningitis in dogs, like in humans, is a very serious, debilitating condition that can even be fatal. The meninges and spinal cord can become inflamed for a number of reasons, ranging from infection with viruses or bacteria to an immune-mediated disorder in which the body's immune system attacks the meninges and spinal cord (and/or brain). Consequently, not every case can be treated in the same way; therefore, it was important to know what type of meningitis Ty had so that he could get proper treatment. The veterinarians and staff took ample time to answer Sara's questions and provided her comfort during this difficult time. Sara knew that, even with treatment, Ty might not survive. The most common meningomyelitis in dogs is related to the immune system attacking the body and the treatment is immunosuppression through several medications which Ty was started on immediately. Early in Ty's treatment, he showed drastic signs of improvement with no signs of relapse.

More than five years have passed since Sara went through this very difficult time, never taking a single day for granted. Sara gives credit to the faculty and staff at the UGA VTH for giving Ty his life back. Today he can be found under the cool shade of an oak tree, smiling happily while watching Val play around him, completely off of his immunosuppression medications and the prednisone that caused him to lose his waistline.

Every day, Sara is thankful to have Ty, who she affectionately calls her "Nugget," by her side. Ty is loved by many, especially Mimi and Grandpa, Sara's parents, who were by his side during surgery. I had the pleasure of meeting Sara, Ty, and little brother, Val, and could not believe that this beautiful guy had gone through such a long and painful few years. Those years only made Ty appreciate life even more today.

Equine
Blood Donor Program

The UGA VTH has had an equine blood donor program in place for over 35 years and has provided blood transfusions that have saved literally hundreds of horses and foals. The equine blood donors are selected for their blood type, health, and gentle disposition. In addition to their job as blood donors, they also double as teaching horses for veterinary students to learn anatomy and examination skills. There are typically four horses in the blood donor program at all times. One horse is housed at the UGA Large Animal Hospital for two weeks at a time followed by six weeks "off duty." When the horse is working, he or she will be on call 24/7. When not working, the horses spend their six weeks on a 200 acre satellite farm owned by the College of Veterinary Medicine, just 15 minutes from campus.

As with human blood transfusions, horses can only donate blood once a month. If the on-call horse reaches its limit, it is rotated back to the farm. The farm also employs two full-time farm managers to take care of the blood donor horses as well as 40 head of cattle and 25 horses that are in the UGA College of Veterinary Medicine (CVM) senior breeding program and are used for teaching and animal health research. The four blood donor horses are usually in service from two to more than ten years. While on call, they are cared for by UGA VTH licensed veterinary technicians and UGA CVM veterinary students rotating through the Large Animal Hospital. Any health issues they may have while in service are attended to by UGA faculty veterinarians just like client-owned animals. Once retired, they are almost always adopted out, in many cases by hospital staff and faculty.

Horses can have one of over 30 different blood types, but the hospital doesn't need to have access to donors with all these blood types. There are a few blood types that are problematic, so the important issue in selecting a blood donor is that they are negative for these problematic types so recipient animals are less likely to have a reaction to the donated blood. They are also screened annually for infectious diseases and other health problems. Because the equine blood donors are screened to ensure they have these less problematic blood types, first-time recipients of blood do not always need a blood type cross-match to the donors. The school is capable of obtaining cross-match testing to identify the most compatible donor for the recipient for less emergency transfusions, such as a planned surgery, or for repeat transfusions. It is also important that the horses in the program have good temperaments as they are often used for teaching new veterinary students about proper horse handling and spend a lot of time in the bustling hospital environment.

Meet Tucker, the equine blood donor on call the day I visited. I asked him to smile and he kindly obliged.

Horses may need blood transfusions due to many different types of injuries, lacerations, surgeries, colic, or foaling-related complications, so you can see why this program serves such a vital role at the hospital. More than 500 horses and foals and thousands of veterinary students have benefited from this program.

Norman & Vera

Norman and his side-kick goat, Vera, have been at the UGA Large Animal Teaching Hospital for 11 years. Norman is able to help sick cows, goats, sheep, alpacas, llamas and even deer or the odd giraffe, by donating some of his rumen (stomach) contents to sick animals. He and Vera also occasionally donate blood to sick cattle and goats. So of all the "staff" at the hospital, they may have saved more lives in that period of time than any of the human faculty or staff.

Cattle are ruminants, meaning they have a very large stomach with four separate compartments that can ferment the hay and grass they eat into usable energy sources. Each compartment has its own specialized duty in the digestive process. Cattle utilize rumination (re-chewing food) as a mechanism of feeding. The most important aspect of maintaining good health in a cow's gut is the proper maintenance of bacteria that live in the rumen. Part of every healthy cow is millions of gut microorganisms – primarily bacteria, protozoa, and some fungi. The millions and millions of bugs that reside in a cow's 20-60 gallon rumen are ultimately responsible for digesting all the plant material the cow consumes. The problem with this symbiotic relationship is that when a cow gets sick so does the bacteria. Just like with humans, bovines need healthy bacteria to digest food and to live but, unlike humans, the bovine needs food to keep the bacteria alive. If a cow doesn't feel well enough to eat, the good bacteria will quickly die. When this happens, without a transfaunation of live bacteria, the cow may also die.

Transfaunation is the process of taking microbes from one source and putting them in another and can be a lifesaver when it comes to a bovine stomach ache. The transfaunation program at the UGA VTH is where Norman is a star.

A permanent port (fistula) was placed in Norman's side into his rumen. This allows easy access to bacteria for transplantation into the sick cow's stomach. The veterinarian or technician (a veterinary nurse) puts on a long plastic glove and slides his or her arm through the port into Norman's stomach to harvest stomach contents containing bacteria which will be life saving to a sick ruminant. These stomach contents containing live, healthy bacteria are then immediately placed into the rumen of the sick animal by quickly passing a stomach tube through the mouth into their  rumen. These bacteria go to work digesting feed in the sick animal's rumen and play an inexpensive but critical role in making them feel better very fast.

Norman and Vera came to the farm eleven years ago when they were quite young. Vera came initially as a companion to Norman as most farm animals do much better with a side-kick, but eventually Vera also became a vital part of the blood donor program for other goats. These famous two at the Large Animal Hospital are well known by all staff and faculty. After so many years of faithful service, they will be retiring to the farm later this year. A replacement calf has already been found and is currently studying under the tutelage of Norman. Her name is Holly. Holly will have quite a reputation to live up to but, if anyone can teach her, it is Norman.

University of Georgia College of Veterinary Medicine

Early Years

In January 1785, led by a movement by Abraham Baldwin, legislature granted a charter for the establishment of the University of Georgia, but sixteen years would pass before the charter was implemented and a site selected near the headwaters of the Oconee River. It would be another 10 years before the first students entered the University. Nine students graduated with degrees on May 31, 1804.

The college grew slowly until after the Civil War but, as the state of Georgia developed as an agricultural hub, Congress provided a grant for the school to teach subjects related to agriculture and mechanical arts and, on May 1, 1872, the Georgia State College of Agriculture and Mechanical Arts began operation.

Unfortunately, Georgia farmers were not prosperous enough to afford higher education during that time-frame because of the low price of cotton. The University trustees reorganized the State College of Agriculture and Mechanical Arts under a separate board of trustees in 1906 and shortly thereafter a department of veterinary science was established and became the eighth department within the State College of Agriculture and Mechanical Arts. Dr. A.G.G. Richardson and Dr. William M. Burson were two of the first department heads, both from the Cincinnati Veterinary College. Much of the early veterinary courses and research was developed around disease control, sanitation and parasites. Dr. Burson supervised the construction of the veterinary hospital building which was located southeast of Conner Hall on the college campus.

Dr. Burson was sensitive to Georgia's need for veterinary curriculum at the University and, in 1916, a veterinary laboratory building was built consisting of two stories and a basement. The basement was set aside for research and the first and second floors were reserved for student instruction. That same year the school announced the offering of the first two years of a proposed four year course leading to the degree of Doctor of Veterinary Medicine. There were eight students in the class.

In 1917, World War I interrupted the program and between 1918 and 1933 financial and political issues caused the school to eventually close with the graduating class of 1933.

Sixty-seven men received the degree of Doctor of Veterinary Medicine from 1921 to the closing of the school in 1933. There were seven veterinarians on the faculty at the time. Many of the students who were still enrolled in the program transferred to other schools of veterinary medicine, including Kansas State University, Texas A & M, and Alabama Polytechnic Institute where they received their degrees.

1946-2015

After the school closed in 1933, a number of individuals and groups kept alive an interest in re-establishing an accredited veterinary school in Georgia, but it was not until after World War II that serious efforts began. During the winter quarter of the 1945-46 school year, many students who had enrolled at the University of Georgia were GI's returning from World War II. These veterans, attending school under the GI Bill, organized the Student Veterans Organization (SVO). This was an organization that had a strong influence on campus life and supported many causes, including reestablishing a course of study in veterinary medicine. Many of these veterans were interested in becoming veterinarians but had been denied entrance to Alabama Polytechnic Institute (now Auburn University), the only institution granting the DVM degree in the Southeast. The SVO pressed the administration to re-establish a veterinary program at the University of Georgia and, in August of 1946, a groundswell of support from students, agricultural organizations, and livestock producers prompted the Board of Regents of the University of Georgia to take official action to re-establish the College of Veterinary Medicine. In September of 1946, two faculty members were employed. A warehouse used by the U.S. Navy during the war was remodeled for laboratory use. Interest in veterinary medicine was great with more than seven hundred applications received for the approximately one hundred positions available. Out-of-state applicants had to be eliminated and half of the positions were reserved for students who had completed pre-veterinary programs and would enroll in the veterinary curriculum. A class of fifty-six was accepted and classes started in the fall quarter of 1946. Dr. Clifford Westerfield was appointed professor of veterinary anatomy and given charge of the program until a dean could be named and he singlehandedly organized the program, developed the early curriculum, outlined the departmental structure, and secured adjunct faculty to assist in teaching. An anatomy laboratory was constructed under the north bleachers of Hardman Hall and courses included bacteriology, animal husbandry, zoology, chemistry, and pharmacy.

In late 1947, following the appointment of a dean, Thomas John Jones, and admission of a second class of students, the architectural firm Claussen and Webster were employed to draw up plans for a new building. Their study, which included the examination and evaluation of several existing veterinary colleges and medical schools, took about nine months.

The new school was to be built on the site where the university sheep barn had been located between 1949 and 1952. These facilities included small and large animal buildings which were primarily used until the new hospital opened in 2015 on College Station Road.

The 1950's started a period of rapid growth in veterinary medical education. While the early years were primarily focused on teaching and clinical service, the following 10 years showed much progress in research and clinical and field studies on new drugs. In 1956, a master's program in veterinary pathology and parasitology was approved and in 1957 the Southeastern Cooperative Wildlife Disease Study approved the study of wildlife disease problems for the state game and fish agencies of the southeastern states. This was the first diagnostic and research service in the United States for the specific purpose of investigating wildlife diseases. Dr. Frank Hayes was chosen the first director and held that position until he retired in 1986.

Veterinary education and the University of Georgia were undergoing many changes in the 1960's. More and more of the country's veterinary faculty members were receiving postgraduate training either in research or in residency specialties or both and the University of Georgia was beginning its move toward becoming a major research institution with the initiation and expansion of graduate programs.

In 1965, Dr. Fred C. Davison became dean of the College of Veterinary Medicine. He was a native Georgian and a 1952 graduate of the University of Georgia College of Veterinary Medicine. He was married to a classmate, Dr. Dianne Castle, and had practiced four and a half years in Marietta before going to Iowa State University as an assistant professor of veterinary physiology. Dr. Davison had a profound influence on the School of Veterinary Medicine as vice-chancellor of the University System of Georgia and then as president of the University of Georgia for the 19 years from 1967-1986.

In September 1968, Dr. Richard B. Talbot, who had been a professor and head of the Department of Physiology and Pharmacology since 1965, was appointed dean. For the next ten years the school continued to expand in terms of programs, physical facilities, and student and faculty numbers. The 1970's began an emphasis on clinical specialties and involvement of clinical faculty becoming board-certified. This would soon become a requirement for tenure of clinical faculty and the University of Georgia faculty would later become leaders at the national level.

At the February 1975 meeting of the Board of Regents, Dr. David P. Anderson was appointed the fifth dean of the College of Veterinary Medicine after serving in several roles at the College from 1969. The appointment of Dr. Anderson began a new era of progress for the college. After he assumed office, the atmosphere became one of mutual trust that served to heighten the morale of faculty and students. His friendly, open-door policy allowed faculty input on program and policy matters. That same atmosphere prevailed until his retirement in 1996.

During the 1980's, the movement toward more specialization was expanded as well as toward specialization related to emergency and critical care, exotic animals and holistic veterinary medicine.

The 1990's represented a decade of expansion with the addition of the Equine Locomotor Center for examination of horses with lameness problems and improvements in radiological services when computerized tomography (CT) capability became available. Additional improvements were achieved when the radiology laboratory was equipped with state-of-the-art imaging equipment allowing computerized radiography, digital fluoroscopy and computer 3-D reconstruction. Also, the 1990's saw changes in clinical instruction with the addition of a single clinician in charge of local clients. Veterinary dentistry and veterinary nutrition became specific disciplines with their own staff, and the exotic service markedly expanded because of the popularity of these species as companions. Applied animal behavioral science emerged as a clinical discipline and a resident position was added in 1999. Most of these changes took place while Keith Prasse was Dean of the College (July 1, 1996 – February 28, 2005).

By the year 2000, after more than 50 years, the College of Veterinary Medicine had risen to national and international prominence with its veterinary graduates in great demand with many becoming leaders in the profession.[1]

In 2005, Dr. Sheila Allen was appointed Dean of the College of Veterinary Medicine. During the more than 11 years she held this position, she was involved in the fundraising and construction of the new Veterinary Medical Center. These efforts took most of her time and required lobbying at the state legislature along with oversight from faculty and staff to make sure that everything possible was done to make the Center the best it could be. Some of the amazing accomplishments in her tenure were:

- The applicant pool for the DVM program doubled to almost 1,200.
- The hospital caseload increased from 17,000 to 27,000 per year.
- The research enterprise grew from $8 million a year to $24 million a year in sponsored awards.
- The outreach activities for the poultry and other food producing industries along with the efforts in reserving wildlife health extended services throughout Georgia.
- The colleges endowment grew from $8 million to $39 million.
- The percentages of under-represented minorities in the DVM student body (18%) and the faculty (21%) doubled, making the UGA College of Veterinary Medicine one of the most diverse in the US.[2]

*1 The history of the University of Georgia College of Veterinary Medicine was extracted from "The Year of Jubilee – A History of the University of Georgia College of Veterinary Medicine." This document was created by J. T. Mercer, Class of 1950 and Robert Duncan, Class of 1950 and published in 2000.

*2 Taken from email to the UGA CVM community from Sheila W. Allen dated August 5, 2016

2015 to present

After more than a dozen years of planning and fund raising, the new University of Georgia Veterinary Teaching Hospital opened on March 2, 2015 at its location at 2200 College Station Road.

The previous Veterinary Hospital, which opened in 1979, handled more than 25,000 visits per year in one of the smallest veterinary teaching hospitals in the United States. Now, the new hospital operates out of a building more than double the size of the old facility and is outfitted with top-of-the line equipment and improved functionality. This new state-of-the-art facility will help attract the highest caliber faculty, staff interns, residents and students to the University of Georgia and further improve clinical teaching, client service and patient care within the Hospital.

Other features of the new Hospital include a flexible design to meet current needs and allow for future expansion; separate emergency entrances for large and small animals; numerous teaching and collaboration spaces; expanded diagnostic imaging capabilities, and radiation therapy for all animal species.

The Veterinary Education Center, which is part of the Veterinary Medical Center campus, features a 160-seat auditorium, an 80-seat technology-enabled active learning classroom, and two smaller classrooms for teaching veterinary students.

The Veterinary Medical Center was designed by Perkins+Will and built by Turner Construction Company.

Third- and fourth-year veterinary students are now located at the new facilities along with all clinical faculty and staff. All other faculty, staff and students remain at the College's original campus, located on D.W. Brooks Drive.

Improvements can be found throughout the facility and range from LED surgery lights to food animal hydraulic chute systems for cattle. Some of the more significant technological advances in the new Hospital include a new and improved linear accelerator. This piece of equipment puts UGA at the forefront of veterinary radiation therapy. A more advanced model than was used in the old hospital allows for a higher dosage of radiation to be delivered to the tumor while sparing more of the surrounding normal tissue from damage than ever before. Not only does this result in fewer side effects each time an animal undergoes radiation therapy, but it also reduces the number of therapy sessions needed to treat tumors that cannot be removed by surgery. For example, the new equipment may allow a small, well-defined brain tumor or a pituitary tumor to be treated with one round of radiation therapy instead of eighteen rounds. The speed of radiation delivery is also about three times faster, shortening the length of the treatment sessions. This new machine also may possibly allow the treatment of other types of tumors including lung and liver, osteosarcoma, and urogenital tumors, such as bladder/prostate tumors. The room that houses this machine was strategically designed so that it would be large enough to allow large animal patients access to this new technology as well.

Other new and improved equipment includes a 64-Slice CT Scanner that allows the Hospital to perform a wider variety of diagnostic procedures and can be used for both small and large animals. It features outstanding image sharpness and clarity combined with amazing speed. Because of these improvements, many small animal patients can be sedated rather than put under general anesthesia. Additionally, it provides instantaneous access to 3-D data by multiple users, which means clinicians and students will be able to review the diagnostic images jointly. The significant improvements of this machine will enhance the patient experience, accuracy of diagnostics, and the learning environment.

The new Hospital also invested in a top-of-the-line 3T MRI machine that features exceptional quality and speed as well as state-of-the-art examination software that can sense motion and decrease artifacts in the final diagnostic images it produces. The open design of the new and improved MRI can accommodate a wide variety of patient shapes and sizes, allowing both large and small animal services to use it. It also allows for images to be taken of the entire body without having to reposition the patient. The machine is quieter and has improved clarity and resolution for optimal cardiac, joint, brain and abdominal imaging. Additionally, its speed has the potential to reduce exam times by up to twenty percent, which also reduces anesthesia times and overall stress of the animal.

Because of the close proximity of the Large and Small Animal Hospitals in this new facility, the ability to share these facilities has saved the patients and staff both time and money.[3]

*3 History of the new facility at 2200 College Station Road was extracted from The University of Georgia Aesculapian Magazine, College of Veterinary Medicine/Spring/Summer 2015 Vol 15, #2.

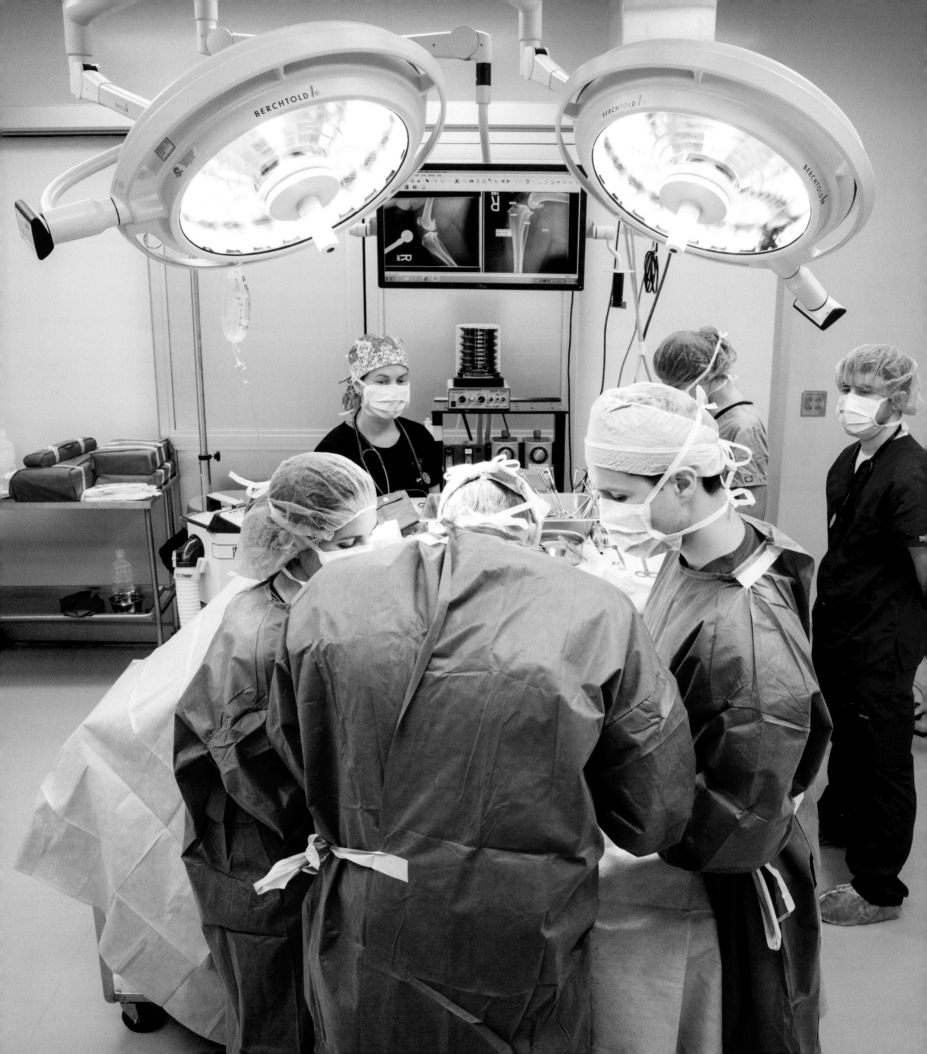

Closing Message

I was first referred to the UGA VTH in 2011 when my dog, Mackenzie was diagnosed with degenerative lumbosacral disease. Because she was such an athlete, we had seen many different veterinarians in both the United States and France over her lifetime, but our introduction to the VTH was really extraordinary. When we entered the small animal hospital for our first appointment, the receptionist, Cheryl, was prepared for our arrival. Everyone we met, from our assigned 4th year student, to the resident, and finally to Mac's neurology surgeon, Dr. Kent, treated us like royalty. They were prepared, informed and caring. Over the next six years, we made many visits to the old and then to the new hospital and I was never disappointed with the care that we both received. Mac was well known at the school, but then, one thing I've learned in writing these "miracle stories," is that everyone I talked to felt their animals were well known, too. What a testament to the special care provided and individual treatment given.

The first story in this book, about Cody's special message, gave me the initial idea for doing the book, but with the next 49 stories, I felt that every story has a special message. Every story in this book and the animal and owner in the story has a special place in my heart and is a statement to the love and care of both the owner and the medical team. I've had more than one animal owner say that, if they got sick, they would like to be brought to the UGA VTH. My hope is that each story will provide the reader with an understanding of the clinical aspect of the diagnosis and treatment of the animal, and a glimpse into the emotional side of the animal and owner, and the recognition that miracles need both sides of the equation to happen.

Mac's death left a hole in my heart. While that hole may not be 100% closed, this past year of meeting most of the story owners in person, all such amazing, caring people, has closed the hole considerably. Each visit provided me much needed therapy, but the real purpose of this book is to raise money for the UGA CVM scholarship program. With my last book, "Travels with Mac 'n' Row," I raised money for animal rescue. With this book, I've now created the Mac and Row Scholarship Fund and all profits will go to that cause. If this book is successful, we can continue to do new editions of the book with new miracle stories every few years with the profits continuing to fund scholarships for years to come. **Let the miracles live on!**

Acknowledgements

My first story in the book, Cody, describes how I got my original idea for creating *Miracles on College Station Road*. I introduced the idea to Kathy Bangle, who at the time was Director of Veterinary External Affairs. She immediately took hold of the idea and began to help me connect with those at the UGA VTH who would help make the idea a reality.

I'd specifically like to thank Karen Aiken and Molly Thomas who helped me identify the stories in the book from the staff and faculty at the VTH and who made initial contact with the story owners to get permission for me to call, write, and publish these miracle stories. Karen and Molly were part of my "immediate team" and I could not have possibly completed this book without them. I am also incredibly grateful to Mac's neurology surgeon and my good friend, Dr. Marc Kent, who edited all the stories for clinical accuracy and contributed information on how the new hospital operates.

Thank you to my dear friend Alison Tinsley, who, like me, lives in a small village in France part of the year and in the States part of the year, for editing my book. I'm better at telling stories than getting commas in the right place. Alison has written a number of books herself and at one time taught Creative Writing classes. Thank you Alison for your time and patience and for being there every time I called with a question or request no matter what side of the world you happened to be on.

Thanks to my wonderful book design team – Daniel and Katarina Devlin. They designed my last book, *Travels with Mac 'n' Row* and graciously agreed once again to help with *Miracles on College Station Road*.

To all the staff, faculty, and students, a special thank you for all you do to make our animal's lives better, and blessings to all who buy and read this book. The profits will benefit an educational scholarship fund for the University of Georgia College of Veterinary Medicine.

Row Henson

Row Henson holds a Bachelor's Degree in Business Administration, with an emphasis in Management and Insurance, from the University of Georgia. At the start of her career, she spent seven years as the head of Human Resources for a non-profit health agency. Ms. Henson then moved on to lead Human Capital Management strategy and product management teams for two of the world's largest software companies. In 1992, she accepted a position at a startup company outside of San Francisco. That startup went on to become the most widely used provider of HCM software in the world – PeopleSoft. Row was instrumental in driving the direction for many years for this award-winning HCM product and for much of its innovation and globalization. All-told, Ms. Henson has been involved in Human Resources and Human Resource Management Systems for over 40 years.

Ms. Henson was voted one of the Top Ten Women in Technology by Computer Currents. She is also the recipient of IHRIM's (International Association for Human Resource Information Management) coveted Summit Award for lifetime achievement in her field. In 2002, Ms. Henson was named the first Visionary of HR Technology at the annual HR Technology Conference. In 2013, Ms. Henson was given the first Lifetime Achievement Award by the Oracle Human Resources User Group.

She retired from PeopleSoft/Oracle Corporation in April, 2013. During her career, Ms. Henson wrote a number of books related to the Human Capital Technology field, but her first "retirement" project was writing *Travels with Mac 'n' Row* about her life with her best friend, Mackenzie. The book, written from the dog's perspective, was first and foremost a love story between the two, but the ultimate goal of the project was to donate the profits from the book's sales to help support animal rescue organizations, a cause near and dear to her heart. "Mac's" book sold out and the profits benefited over 80 different animal rescue organizations worldwide.

Today, she divides her time between the south of the United States and the south of France. Her famous dog, Mac, is no longer with her but lives on in the books that she inspired.

A special thanks
to the amazing professionals
that help keep our animals healthy.